A Year in Addlestone

TIM DYSON

Michael O'Mara Books Ltd

First published in Great Britain in 1993 by
Michael O'Mara Books Limited, 9 Lion Yard,
Tremadoc Road, London SW4 7NQ

A CIP catalogue record for this book is available ·
from the British Library

ISBN 1 85479 941 X

Typeset by Florencetype Limited, Kewstoke, Avon
Printed and bound in England by Cox & Wyman, Reading

January

I 'ad once loved Provence. From a leetle boy I loved ze lavatory-brush pines, ze maquis, ze wild boar chasse, ze leetle bistros on ze coast between my home village, le Rayol-Canadel and St Tropez – not to mention ze bottomless beaches in ze summer. When I was a youngster, ze Mistral used to cool my adolescent passions as I cycled from peasant cottage to peasant cottage, delivering porno magazines from my grand-mother's newsagent shop.

My family 'ad lived in ze Var for centuries, but life was 'ard. I 'ad been forced to abandon ze land of my forefathers and plunge myself into ze cruel world of advertising to write TV commercials for soaps and toilet cleaners. By ze time I was forty I was producing advertising campaigns worth millions of francs.

But I was bored. Money meant nothing to me any more. I wanted a quiet life, away from ze 'eart attacks and chaos of advertising lies. I wanted tranquillity and culture. I wanted to flee ze hubbub of Provence. I was fed up wiz ze Côte d'Azur, and ze lush 'ills towering behind my stupid village. Fed up wiz ze Massif des Maures teaming wiz wild life, mimosa and bougainvillaea. Fed up wiz ze secluded sandy beaches and ze boring night-life of St Tropez just a condom's throw down ze coast.

So I resigned from my multinational ad agency and my multi-national salary, and chose to buy a rustic cottage in ze wilds of rural England. My wife, Absinthe, and I chose Five Station Approach, Addlestone, in ze 'eart of ze province of Surrey, next to ze soothing waters of ze River Wey. Ah, Station Approach; ze Promenade des Anglais of ze English Riviera! Addlestone, a quaint 'istoric village on ze outskirts of Heathrow, wizin a British Rail Travelcard of London itself. What could be more romantic?

At last, I could be 'appy and relaxed. No more ze stressful anxieties of Provence. No more ze oppressive sunshine and bottomless tourists zat 'ad blighted my life since childhood. Addlestone, ze Mecca of my dreams: cool temperatures, refresh-

1

ing rain, white Christmases, quaint pubs and friendly peasants. Not to mention ze famous Addlestone take-away cuisine and ze generous Giro Cheque.

Absinthe and I arrive at Heathrow by Concorde on New Year's Eve. Ze trip to Addlestone by taxi takes only twenty minutes and costs only seventy pounds. We 'ave arrived in paradise – enfin!

Unfortunately, paradise 'as no lighting or 'eating! It is dark, cold, damp and windy. Five Station Approach is very charming, wiz old-fashioned fireplaces to allow ze freezing wind down ze chimneys to air-condition ze rooms. What clever Addlestone peasant cunning!

We try to phone ze estate agent about ze lack of light and 'eat, but 'is wife says 'e is 'down ze pub'. Unfortunately 'is pub is many miles from Addlestone, so we leave our suitcases in ze master bedroom and go round to ze nearest pub, ze Dog and Duck, to find an 'elping 'and.

Ze Dog and Duck is a very friendly, quaint old pub wiz a formica bar and plastic chairs to match. It is full of shouting, red-faced peasants and artisans spending zer last Giro Cheques of ze year, we discover. Ze barman is a typical British character, called Tony, from Portugal: 'is accent is easier for me to understand zan ze Addlestonians. Everybody calls 'im 'Tone Deaf', because 'e never listens to 'is customers.

Tone introduces Absinthe and I to Kev, who is a famous local 'andyman, but Tone 'as to interpret 'is accent for us. Kev agrees to go back wiz us to ze cottage to 'elp our problem but, because it is New Year's Eve, 'e insists on 'aving two more pints of ze famous local Gutterspew Ale first.

Two hours later we 'elp Kev down ze road to ze cottage where 'e just looks under ze stairs – which 'e strangely calls 'apples'. 'E flicks a switch and in a flash ze lights come on and ze 'eating starts working! Quel miracle! Kev is a real smart biscuit.

''Ow much do I owe you, Kev?' I ask, as I pull out a fifty-pound note.

'Nuffink, mon brave. But another pint or three might ease the pain!' 'E winks and gives me an 'efty nudge wiz 'is elbow, which sends me reeling across ze room. Absinthe and I 'elp Kev back to ze Dog and Duck, where 'e asks for a pint of Gutterspew with a gold chaser. I 'ad been studying my English phrase book, but I didn't understand Kev very well.

'By ze byway, Kev, what is a "gold chaser"? I 'ave never 'eard of zat.'

'A large scotch to nullify the effect of the beer.' Kev is obviously looking forward to it. 'It's rhyming slang, see. We use it all the time in the Dog and Duck. "Gold's" short for "gold watch", that rhymes wiv scotch – scotch whisky, see. But you just say the first part, "gold", wivout the rhyming bit, "watch". Like I did at your place, remember? I said "apples" for "apples and pears", means "stairs". Geddit? It's a large "gold watch" if you don't mind, mon brave.'

'Ow stupid I was, I think, not to 'ave taken ze advanced English course at my lyceé in St Tropez!

'Yer know this pub's name is rhyming slang, too,' Kev goes on. 'Dog and Duck – geddit?'

'Do you get it, my dear?' I raise my eyebrows at Absinthe.

'Not at all, mon cher Ash.' Ash is ze short version she gives me for Achille.

Kev is triumphant. 'E smashes me in ze ribs wiz 'is rugby elbow: 'What yer gonna give yer missus when you get between the sheets tonight?'

'A goodnight kiss?' I venture.

'Naah, mon brave ami.' Kev raises 'is forearm wiz 'is fist clenched in ze famous European Community salute. I understand 'is basic meaning but cannot work out ze rhyming between 'screw' and Dog and Duck.

Absinthe blushes and laughs behind 'er 'and: 'I'll tell you later, Ash mon chou.' I 'ated 'er using ze short form of my name, but it is in revenge for me calling 'er 'ma petite poubelle', my little dustbin.

'I'm sorry, Kev,' I apologized for my incompetence in English. Kev gives me another wink and elbow in ze ribs. 'You'll be allright tonight. Ash, mon brave ami!'

I try to restart ze conversation. 'Your French is very good, Kev. Where did you learn it, may I ask?'

'No trouble at all, mon Ash: from the *Allo Allo* TV series.'

'Zat's amazing!' I rejoin. 'I learnt my English from ze very same programme when it was shown on French TV. Congratulations!'

Ze pub is livening up. It is getting towards midnight and ze Nouvelle Année. It is too late to go back to ze cottage and 'ave ze Provençal wild boar wiz Soixante-Neuf du Pape wine we brought specially from France for ze celebration of Réveillon.

We decide to tuck in to typical Addlestone peasant fare – a brace of corned-beef sandwiches wiz mayonnaise, washed down wiz Babycham to drink in ze New Year. Ze landlord of ze Dog and Duck, 'Bruiser' Reade zey call 'im, a big man whose stomach 'as seen many mega-litres of ze local Gutterspew Ale, switches on ze TV at five to twelve so we can all 'ear ze midnight chimes of ze famous Big Ben. Ze inmates of ze Dog and Duck fall reverently silent as Big Ben ticks ze final seconds to ze New Year. Suddenly, midnight is struck and ze whole pub goes wild. Everybody toasts each other with glasses of Babycham, and a funny man on ze TV, wearing a chequered mini-skirt, leads us all in ze traditional 'Auld Lang Syne', which Kev tells me is Scottish for ze old England 'V' sign, whatever zat is.

We all join 'ands and 'old each other up as we try to dance across ze linoleum floor to ze 'Old England Sign'. Kev gives Absinthe a Castlemaine XXXX kiss on ze lips and a bra-breaking 'ug. I escape wiz a sloppy kiss on ze cheek.

''Ow about a New Year kiss for yer new English mate, my Froggie friend?' Kev offers me 'is sweating stubbly cheek and I comply. 'E puts 'is arm round my neck and I start losing oxygen. But it is all in ze fun, ze wonderful fun of rural life in picturesque Addlestone.

Absinthe and I are 'appy. 'Appy to be in paradise among ze genuine fun-lovers of zis village fantastique. We 'ave been accepted into local society, le Tout Addlestone. Everybody is calling us ze 'Farting Froggies'. What a wonderful British sense of 'umour! It makes everything worthwhile.

Absinthe and I 'elp Kev to 'is taxi and meander back to ze cottage to sleep. But we cannot wait to wake up later on New Year's Day. I kiss Absinthe on ze cheek 'Bonne nuit, ma poubelle. Au revoir, Provence. Bonne année, Addlestone!'

We awake just before midday to ze sound of trains shunting behind ze railway station. Ah, ze sound of ze famous British Rail! So advanced, I 'ave 'eard, zat ze British Government cannot 'andle it any more, and 'ave decided to sell it off to ze public. Strange, I think, because surely ze British public owns British Rail already?

'Absinthe, ma petite poub,' I call from ze tiny bathroom, 'Kev 'as invited us to meet all 'is friends at ze Dog and Screw. We should go.'

'It's ze Dog and *Duck*, mon grand chou!' She corrects me. 'I 'ope 'e remembers from last night. Let's go.'

Ze Dog and Duck is full. We find Kev, who looks very pale and 'as three pints of beer in front of 'im.

'Why do you 'ave so many pints in front of you, Kev?' I ask.

'Ooooh, Frog-Ash, me mate, I've gotta get rid of this 'angover somehow. Fairly killing me it is.'

'I don't feel top-hole myself, Kev. I cannot take all zat Babycham. What would you suggest? Ze hair of ze bitch?'

'Naah!' Kev pulls a face. 'What you need is a dose of this.' He nods towards ze now one-and-a-'alf pints in front of 'im.

'Addlestone's world-famous Gutterspew Ale. Powerful stuff. Brewed down by the station, near you.'

'Oh, so zat is ze smell. I thought it was a problem wiz ze drains.'

'Naah, mate. It may not smell like it, but it's pure nectar. I suggest you and your missus, Absent, neck a couple o' jars. You'll feel like a million dollars again.'

'What is ze exchange rate between pounds and dollars now?' I quip wiz a wry smile. Kev ignores me so I order a pint and a 'alf of Gutterspew for Absinthe and me. Kev finishes 'is third pint so I order another one for 'im, too.

'Let me introduce you, my new-found Frogs, to some of the great characters of Addlestone. Rodge!' 'e shouts along ze bar, 'Come 'ere and meet two rare creatures: two intelligent Froggies who've chosen Addlestone as their new 'ome. Ash and Absent Blancmange.'

'Actually, ze name is Mange-Tout. It's a vegetable, you know.' I explain.

'Sorry, Ash. Rodge, Monsieur Mange-Tout.'

Rodge 'olds out 'is 'and. 'Cosmic! You're not related to that Belgian detective, by any chance, are you – you know, that Poirot on telly?'

'No, it's a different strain,' I try to smile.

'Rodge is our resident accountant and philosopher, ain't yer, Rodge. A rare combination. We call 'im Rodge the Dodge.' Kev winks and nudges me in ze ribs wiz 'is beefy elbow.

Rodge smiles proudly. 'My motto is "Cogito Ergo Sum", which being freely translated is Latin for "I Think I am an Accountant". It was one of our philosophers who said it first, Monsieur Blancmange-Tout. I'm sure you 'ave 'eard of

Des Carts? Much cleverer than that Pole, Voltaire, in my opinion. But any time you need a bit of "you know what" wiv your accounts, just let me know. They don't call me Rodge the Dodge for nothing. I work in the Dog and Duck Mondays, Wednesdays and Fridays, and in the Berkeley Arms Tuesdays and Thursdays. Cosmic to meet you, Mr and Mrs Blancmange-Tout.'

And wiz zat, 'e returns to ze company of an attractive teenage blonde girl at ze end of ze bar – I assume 'is daughter – and gives 'er a very affectionate kiss.

'Great blokes 'ere, Ash. I'll make sure you meet them all.', says Kev', proud of 'is knowledge and influence. 'Know somefink, Ash,' he continues, 'I've got great plans for Addlestone. I'm gonna stand for the Council next election. Can't wait to get rid of that toffee-nosed aristoprat who's our councillor now, Sir St John Pumpkin-Smythe.'

'When is ze next election, Kev?'

'Next month, my Froggie friend. Maybe you and Absent could do some canvassing for me?' 'E raises 'is eyebrows and smiles.

'Of course, Kev, we should be delighted,' I reply.

'Hey, Ash,' 'e nudges me again, 'there's another Addlestone illumination you 'ave to meet!' 'E beckons fiercely to a big man in ze corner of ze pub. 'Is shirt is wide open and 'e 'as an even hairier chest zan Kev, and wears even more gold chains. 'E zig-zags towards us.

Kev introduces us, getting our name right for ze first time.

'This is Rod, Ash. Rod the Hod, 'cos 'e's a freelance bricky. Say 'ello, Rod.' Rod grunts. 'Just look at that chest – like a burst-open sofa! Rod's setting up on 'is own – and, Ash, goin' into Europe! 'E's setting up a "Rod's Hod Hire". Cor, it ain't 'alf 'ard sayin' all them aitches! Is that right. Rod?' Rod grunts again. 'E is obviously missing 'is pint of Gutterspew.

'Rod's 'Od 'Ire,' Kev continues, 'will rent out 'ods to con-struction companies, large and small, all over the Common Market – AND, my old Ash tree, *Eastern Europe and the ex-Russia*! Isn't that right, me old cocker?'

Rod grunts and scratchs 'is sofa.

'I'll need a facsimile machine.' Rod suddenly speaks. 'Know where I can get one at a discount, Kev? Yer know?'

'Might be able to get yer one off a second-hand lorry. I'll look around for yer, Rod.' Kev gives 'im another of 'is prolific winks.

6

'Better get back to the missus, then. See yer.' Rod zig-zags back to ze corner of ze pub to rejoin a lady wiz curly bleach-blonde 'air and a low-cut blouse which shows she is well endowed.

'Watch yer eyes. Ash,' Kev leers at me. 'Technically she's not 'is missus. He picked 'er up after she won the Addlestone Miss Cleavage Contest two years ago. Actually it's called the Miss Addlestone Beauty Contest, but the judges only measure one criterium, know what I mean?' 'E laughs loudly and nudges me so 'ard 'e sends me reeling across ze bar and into ze Gents, straight into ze urinal.

While I am zer I take advantage of ze facilities, and notice zat ze loo paper is 'Addlestone Sewage Works – Recycled'. Ze paper is as white as can be expected in ze circumstances. Ze slogan on ze wrapper says 'Save a Tree with Every Wipe'. I return to ze bar just in time to put my 'ands over Absinthe's ears before Kev delivers ze punch line to one of 'is jokes.

Kev finally stops laughing at 'is joke and manages to drown another pint of Gutterspew. 'There's another geezer you must meet, Ash. We call 'im 'The Brain' 'cos 'e's setting up the Addlestone Arts Festival for us next month. Oy, Brain!' Kev shouts to a dapper man coming out of ze Gents, wearing a spotted red bow-tie, a yellow-striped suit and brown-and-white brogues. 'E comes over to us at ze bar.

'Ash, meet The Brain – or by 'is proper name. Brian Damage. The Brain will be chairman of our Arts Festival.'

Ze Brain 'as a small rolled cigarette in 'is mouth, through which 'e is coughing all ze time, and another cigarette tucked between 'is ear and 'is straggly white 'air. What characters zese are in Addlestone! I must write a book about zem.

'Enchanté, Monsieur,' ze Brain manages between coughs. 'Ain't that Frog lingo for "Wotcha, mate"? I apologize for my wheeze but I've caught an infection of the bronicles.'

'E 'as a coughing fit, which 'e manages wizout losing ze rolled cigarette between 'is lips.

'In honour of this grand meeting to discuss the *French* contribution to the Arts Festival,' Kev gives me a 'efty nudge, 'I suggest we adjourn to the Itie restaurant for a spot of lunch – on the Arts Festival budget, of course, if that's all right, Brain?'

Ze Brain coughs 'is assent.

'Which restaurant is zat, Kev?'

'Addlestone's first Itie restaurant. La Cloaca Maxima, named after the famous fast-food chain in Rome.'

We walk a few yards down ze High Street to ze Cloaca Maxima.

'I'm 'aving the Vivaldi Special. Quattro Stagoni. What'll you lot 'ave?' Kev asks wiz a generous smile.

'I'll go for the Lice Spaghetti,' ze Brain smiles through 'is cigarette.

'What's that?' Kev is confused.

'Spaghetti al Pesto, you royal ignoramus!' Ze Brain laughs through 'is cigarette.

'Thanks, Brain. What about Ash and Absent?'

'Please, if ze Arts Festival chairman agrees, I would like one Spaghetti Aglio Olio and Pepperoncini for myself and, for my wife, ze Pizza alla Carbonara wiz garlic bread and chips.'

'Cor, Ash, I can't pronounce all that wop garbage. We'd better call the Italian waiter. Garkon!' 'E shouts and ze waiter comes to ze table. Kev orders: 'One Vivaldi's Stagoni, one Spaghetti Pesticide. And for you two Froggies?'

I give ze waiter my order but 'e doesn't seem to understand, even though 'e 'as dark 'air and a bushy black moustache.

'Are you Italian?' I ask.

''Certo, matey. From Napoli. But I was-a brung up in downtown Addlestone-a. Maybe you justa give-a me the menu numbers, okay?'

I give 'im ze numbers and Kev orders six pints of Gutterspew lager, and a bottle of Italian Nasti Spewmanti for me and Absinthe.

Ze food arrives and Kev asks ze Brain to explain ze plans for ze Arts Festival. When 'e 'as stopped blowing ash over 'is spaghetti, 'e begins 'is story between mouthfuls, amazingly wizout taking ze cigarette out of 'is mouth.

'Well, me Froggie mates, Addlestone's gonna become the cultural centre of the whole of England. We're not gonna be dominated by those nobs in London any more. But we're gonna do it in stages.'

'E coughs and loses a strand of spaghetti from 'is mouth, but manages not to lose 'is cigarette. Finally 'e speaks.

'We'll start wiv the Addlestone Poetry Festival next month, followed by the Addlestone Arts Festival. Then, in March, we 'ave the All-Fringe Theatre Festival. And at a later date, yet to be fixed, the Addlestone Eurovision Karaoke Song Contest. We're gonna be quite busy, I can tell you, mon matelot. If yet like, when I've paid the bill 'ere – or rather the Addlestone Arts Council 'as,' 'e winks. 'We can adjourn to Addlestone's new wine bar, the Coq au Vin, known locally as the "Brewer's Droop". We can 'ave a jar of "quelque chose" and meet Addlestone's star rap poet, recently imported from Uganda. E's chairman of the Poetry Festival next month. 'Is name is Winston Thatcher and 'e's an expert on Shakespeare, so we call 'im Andronicus, 'cos 'e's always Titus. If yer get my meaning.'

At ze Coq au Vin, Absinthe and I are informed zat Addlestone 'as its own vineyard! What a magnifique place Addlestone is!

Ze Brain offers me a choice between Addlestone's two world-famous wines: Château Plonqueur red, or Entre Deux Merdes white. I choose ze Plonqueur and Absinthe chooses ze Merdes. Kev and ze Brain order vintage Gutterspew lager. Suddenly, an African-looking gentleman walks in and says 'ello to ze Brain and Kev.

Ze Brain introduces us. 'Monsieur and Madam Blancmange-Tout, please meet our resident rap poet, Winston Thatcher from Uganda.' We shake 'ands and ask ze gentleman to recite one of 'is rap poems.

'Sure, man. This is a number I'll be presentin' at the Festival. It goes like this, man:

> 'Don't think I am an *idi*-ot
> I never 'ave been *amin* lot.
> I fled Uganda and by heck
> I'm gonna get my giro cheque.'

'Bril, Winston!' Absinthe and I applaud. 'We cannot wait for ze Festival. Incidentally,' I turn to Kev, 'Kev, when can I expect to receive my Giro Cheque?'

Kev is surprised: 'Should be no problem, mato. I get twenty-five a week. Yours is easy-peasy.'

It is late and we all say Bonne Nuit. Absinthe and I stroll back to Five Station Approach. Our first day in Addlestone. What characters! What a rustic, peasant paradise!

Ze next morning we wake up to ze sound of shunting trains and ze aroma of ze Gutterspew Brewery. From ze bedroom window I see ze watery sun rise over ze Safeway's car park, ze Police station and ze Runnynose Council block. Another glorious day dawns over Addlestone. I rush down to ze super-market for a loaf of freshly frozen sliced bread and a fresh tin of baked beans, ze typical English breakfast. 'Ow did I ever think croissants and cognac were a proper start to ze day in Provence?

Absinthe and I are very 'appy. Despite burst water pipes and failed central 'eating, we are kept warm, like all Addlestonians, by Tandoori take-aways and Cloaca Maxima pizzas. January 'as passed like a dream.

TONE DEAF

February

It is February, and ze wonderful British snow 'as fallen, clothing Addlestone in a mantle of white. I 'ave never seen ze Safeway's car park look so beautiful. From ze bedroom window you cannot even see ze railway tracks under ze lovely white blanket.

Absinthe and I decide to go for a promenade. Ze children are 'aving what zey call a 'snow-bollock' fight. Outside ze Runnynose Council offices a giant snow woman 'as been built, complete wiz two pomegranates and 'alf a fig. I think it is a promotion for ze local fruiterer, 'Rotty' Naylor, but I am wrong. When we get to ze warmth of ze Dog and Duck, Kev explains.

'Naah, Frog-Ash! It's nothing to do wiv Rotty. It's the Addlestone Feminist League. They call themselves "Ad Lib" – Addlestone Liberation, geddit? They build a female snowman every time it snows.'

I am disappointed: 'I thought Addlestone was free from spiritual pollution, Kev. 'Ow many women are in ze Ad Lib?'

Kev pulls a face: 'Only two. Ma wife and me mother-in-law. But that's enough. It's a whole bleedin' army.'

'Zat's rough, Kev. 'Ow do you survive?'

'I don't survive, mon brave Frog-leg, except when I'm in 'ere.'

'Are zey very militant?' I ask.

'Militant? Not 'alf!' Kev gets me to order 'im a fourth pint of Gutterspew. 'Cheers, Frog-face! Militant? They're cosmic! Only the other week, me old Ash tree, I opened my newspaper to look at Page Three as usual, and what do I find?'

'What do you find, Kev?' I am all a go-go.

'Yer know what they'd done? They'd stubbed their fags out on the young lady's delicate parts to spoil my pleasure. I'm an animal lover and I call that obscene, don't you agree, Ash?'

'Do you think zey could ever be ethnically cleansed, Kev?'

'No chance, Frog mate! They're incleansable, that lot. Yer know another thing?' 'E comes close and whispers gruffly in my ear, nearly blowing my brains out. 'They even put salt in my

11

female dildo that I'd paid a fortune for in Soho 'cos it's got all the electrics and sound effects. I can't tell yer 'ow much grief and pain that caused! I think I need another Gutterspew, Ash.' I order 'im one more and 'e continues.

'As part of their campaign, my mother-in-law makes obscene phone calls to all the men she doesn't like in the High Street. She breathes 'eavy like, yer know, and when they're all excited by 'er dirty chat, she changes 'er voice all posh and says she's a police officer and she's coming round to arrest 'em for listening to porno messages. Scares the bollocks off 'em. Then she and me missus laugh themselves to sleep.'

'Zat is 'orrible, Kev. I think you are very brave to put up wiz zat agronomy.'

'What's worse,' Kev carries on, 'the mother-in-law's probably gonna stand at the next Council election this month. That's why I've *gotta* stand as an independent, 'cos if she gets in it'll be bollock decimation all over Addlestone. The lights'll go out for ever.'

'You must excuse us, Kev. Absinthe and I are going to try ze new Cambodian restaurant zat 'as just opened in ze High Street, ze Pol Pot-Pourri. Zey say ze meat is very fresh. See you later!'

We 'ave a delicious meal at ze Pol Pot. Ze meat is very red and tasty, just 'ow we 'Froggies' like it. We wash it down wiz zer specially imported Cambodian red wine, St Rivière Sang Rouge. It 'as a lot of body.

At ze end of ze meal ze proprietor offers us a night hat. I ask what cognac zey 'ave, but ze owner, Phnom Pen Nib, kindly suggests we try ze famous English pastis which 'e imports all ze way from Cornwall. 'Ow exciting to find pastis in Addlestone amongst all ze other delights!

'What is zis pastis called?' I ask excitedly.

Phnom Pen Nib replies: 'It is imported from Cornwall. It is called "Cornish Pastis".'

'E only charges us eight pounds a glass, which is very reasonable considering ze import tax. We drink a toast to ze life in Addlestone and retire to Five Station Approach, tired but 'appy.

Next day, I decide to do some research into ze 'istory of ancient Addlestone down ze library. I must know about my new roots. Ze library is famous for its large selection of literature, from Enid Blyton to Hank Janson.

I make ze most amazing discovery. Ze origin of ze word, Addlestone, is in fact French! Addlestone is full of surprises! In ze 1950s, when Addlestone was just a row of mud 'uts – some of which can be seen to zis day – our glorious French navy sent an expedition force up ze River Wey to capture ze Golden Fleas, or as we say in French, ze 'Puces d'Or'. Ze Golden Fleas used to perform at ze Addlestone Circus, and zey were called Golden because zey performed tricks zat only rich men could see since zey were so tiny and so fast.

Ze Golden Fleas were captured and put in a Bryant and May matchbox. But, unfortunately, our glorious matelots fell in love wiz an Addlestone girl – a distant relative of Essex girl, but wizout even one GCSE. She was one and zey were many but she managed to keep our matelots 'appy for many years.

Zey forgot zer 'omeland and settled on ze banks of ze River Wey. Zey used to go to ze local pub, Ye Olde Dogge and Ducke, where ze locals used to warn zem, 'One more drink and you'll be stoned'. But ze matelots always asked for 'an extra stone'. Which is why zey called zer settlement on ze banks of ze River Wey, 'Add-Le-Stone'. What a fascinating story!

It is Sunday, and Absinthe and I go to ze local Free Range Church of Addlestone, which 'as an ancient tradition of inviting ze local peasants to bring zer farm animals wiz zem to share in ze service. It is a very moving experience. Ze service is led by ze Reverend Trevor La Font, know as Trev ze Rev, and 'is verger, E. C. Surplice. Ze farmers sing 'Ze Common Market is my Shepherd, I shall not want for a Subsidy' and all ze animals join in. At communion time ze congregation receives a free-range egg and a sip of Gutterspew Ale. When ze lesson is read about ze return of ze Prodigal Son, all ze cows cry. At ze end of ze service. Absinthe and I are introduced to Trev ze Rev and E. C. Surplice.

'Do you not have an animal to bring to the next service?' ze Rev asks me.

'Actually, we 'ave a goldfish. Is zat allowed?' I reply.

'Of course,' says ze Rev, 'as long as it doesn't make too much noise.'

We stroll off to ze Dog and Duck for a Sunday midday drink. Kev is groaning over ze bar wiz three pints in front of 'im.

''Ow are you, Kev?' I ask.

'Don't ask, Frog features! I'll 'ave to neck these three Gutterspews before I join the human race.'

Ze sound of coughing at ze entrance announces ze arrival of Brian Damage. ''Ello, Brain. 'Ow are you today?' I ask.

'Not too good, Ash. Me bronicles are givin' me murder.' 'E sips 'is Gutterspew, keeping 'is cigarette in 'is mouth.

'What about the Poetry Festival, Brain?' Kev suddenly perks up, after 'is fifth pint.

'That's why I'm 'ere,' ze Brain spits out between coughs and swigs of Gutterspew. 'We 'ave to 'ave a committee meetin' tomorrow to fix the planifications. It'll be you, Kev, me, Rodge the Dodge and, of course, Andronicus – if 'e's not too Titus. And, if I may make so bold, Monsieur Blancmange, we should be very honoured if your good self would join us on the committee to impart your French culturial expertise?'

'I should be time-honoured, Mr Damage. When is ze meeting?'

Ze Brain waits to ze end of a coughing fit before re-starting.

'At three in the afternoon, 'ere in the Snug, just through there.' 'E gestures wiz 'is cigarette – still in 'is mouth – towards ze little room just beyond ze Gents. 'Oh, and Kev. I think we need a publicity campaign, so I'll get our resident adman, J. Walter Connall, to come along as well. We definitely need an advertising slogan. We can use the same one to push the Art Festival and the All-Fringe Theatre Festival as well. You agree, Kev?'

Kev belches 'is agreement. 'By the way,' 'e manages between burps, 'don't forget I've booked us all in for the visit next Friday to the Gutterspew brewery. You gonna join us, me old Ash tray?'

'I should be charmed,' I reply wiz a smile.

'Should be a good day,' Kev goes on. 'We do a tour of the brewery and then they take us to the famous, ancient Addlestone sewage works where all their beer is recycled. I think I need another beer after all that intellectual conversation. You're in the chair Ash, mate.'

I buy 'im another pint, and discover to my delight zat ze Dog and Duck is now selling Cornish Pastis, so I order a quick one for myself and an Addlestone Recycled Spring Water for Absinthe.

'Ash, me French cocker, 'ave yer listened to our new radio station, Radio Addlestone?'*

---

* A pirate station broadcasting from a barge on the Wey canal.

'Not yet, Kev. Where is it on ze face?'

'On the *dial*, Ash. 87.9 FM. Our very own station! The Brain managed to get this out-of-work local TV presenter, Jerry Logan, to take on the job as 24-hour DJ.'

''Ow does 'e sleep, Kev?' I ask.

'No problem. 'E nods off during the records and the news flashes. And there's some pre-recorded programmes that give 'im 'alf hours at a stretch. It'll all sponsored by the Addlestone Rotundary Club and the local traders in the High Street. You should tune in, mate.'

'Okay, Kev, we'll take your advice and go back to Station Approach right away. See you later.'

Absinthe and I struggle back through ze brown slush to our lovely terrace cottage.

Radio Addlestone is fantastique! We listen all evening to zer very original programmes. First zey 'ave a movie review, by Norm Boring. 'E plays clips from famous silent movies. You can 'ear ze cinema organ accompaniment and imagine ze pictures. But because we cannot see ze subtitles, Norm reads zem out for us. 'Ow clever! We listen to ze classics by Lillian Gish and Claudette Colbert. Zen, as a special treat, Norm plays ze very sexy movie, *And God Created Woman* wiz Brigitte Bardot, and 'e dares to broadcast ze famous nude scene! Absinthe gets very jealous when I get excited.

Later, after tea, we listen to ze famous Addlestone phone-in game show, *Spot ze Ball*. Every picture is described in detail and you 'ave to choose from squares A to Z and one to twenty where ze ball is and phone in your choice of square. Quite a game of skill!

At nine o'clock zer is a brilliant magic show wiz ze famous British conjurer, Danny Paul. 'E performs ze most amazing tricks, including sawing 'imself in 'alf. Only one trick fails. 'E chains 'is accountant in an under-water cage, but 'e fails to escape. Everybody is upset except Danny, 'imself. I wonder why.

Finally, at midnight, Jerry Logan introduces *Goodnight Addlestone*, which specializes in ze new Sludge Music. Jerry is offering, as a promotion for ze programme, egg-timer alarms from Taiwan, so zat you can wake up in ze morning wizout ze noise of a regular alarm clock. It is perfect for Addlestone because nobody wants to wake up anyway.

15

And so to bed, in eager anticipation of ze Poetry Festival meeting tomorrow.

I arrive at ze Dog and Duck early at five to three. Eventually, at three-thirty, Kev, ze Brain, Rodge and Andronious arrive wiz a very smart man in a pin-striped shell suit, who is introduced to me as J. Walter Connall, ze local advertising agency whiz-kid, called Wally by zose who know 'im.

Ze chairman, ze Brain, opens ze proceedings, between coughs. 'Welcome, all, to this planification meeting of the 'istoric first Addlestone Poetry Festival. I extend a special 'ello to our new Froggie friend, Ash Blancmange, who is 'ere to advise us on French cultural matters. Although 'is advice may not be vital for the Poetry Festival, because it'll all be in English, I'm sure 'e will be indisposable for when it comes to the Art Festival later on.'

'Thank you, Mr Damage,' I acknowledge 'is welcome.

'We're all agreed the Poetry Festival takes place on the thirtieth of February. Okay?'

Everybody nods between sips of Gutterspew.

'Right, then, the only thing to be decided is the advertising slogan to put the Festival on the map. What's your opinion, Rodge?'

'I think it should be: "Addlestone is Cosmic".'

Ze Brain fights through 'is coughing fit: ''Ow about you, Andronicus?'

'Well, man, we mustn't be too rectangular, man. We've gotta be groovy and grunge, man. 'Ow about "There's nothin' that matters 'xcept Izombic Pentameters"?'

Wally Connall intervenes. 'Sorry, chappies, but the slogan has to direct visitors from all over the country to the cultural centre of Addlestone, so it must flag the location to help visitors find us. I recommend, because we're just off Junction 11 on the M25: "Junction Eleven is Closest to Heaven".'

We are all impressed. Ze Brain calls for a vote and Wally's slogan wins ze acceptance of ze committee. Everything else is agreed and we prepare for ze mega poetry event.

When ze day arrives we all gather in ze First Brownie Pack Nissen Hut Hall. Ze turn-out is small, though ze Dog and Duck is full. Andronicus recites many of 'is famous rap poems, which are well received by ze blue-rinse, Zimmerframe audience. As a finale, Andronicus introduces an Addlestonian, Bill Wordsworthless, who declaims a dramatic monologue entitled, 'The Sad Tale of an Addlestone Maid'.

'This is the tale of an Addlestone Maid
    Who was worried about 'er virginity;
She was all of fifteen and never been laid,
    So she went to the Church, Holy Trinity.
She was very depressed 'cos she not been caressed,
    But she plucked up courage to go to Confessional;
Whatever 'appened, she knew she'd be blessed,
    'Cos she knew the young priest was professional.
Said the priest, "Give your hand, my child, it'll be nice.
    You'll touch the Promised Land you've never seen,
You'll feel the joy of Paradise;
    Just pass your lily-white fingers through the screen.
"Though the screen between us is a barrier,
    Your hand is divine like Maradona;
My child, I'll give you the hand of God, so you know what
    to expect when they marry yer.
    Can you feel the warm sceptre of our Madonna?"
So they exchanged hands without reading the bands.
    The Addlestone Maid cried out 'er confession
And squeezed his sceptre till his emotion over-swept 'er,
    While his Hand of God made its own impression!
Though the Addlestone Maid didn't get laid in the Church
    of the Holy Trinity,
    She always went to confess in 'er Sunday dress,
And 'er Father Confessor continued to press 'er;
    So at last she lost it all in the vicinity.'

Ze Nissen hut applauds furiously.

'Thank you, man,' Titus congratulates Mr Wordsworthless.

Mr Wordsworthless, slips elegantly to ze floor and is 'elped back on to 'is seat.

Andronicus closes ze evening wiz a tribute to 'Rap Crap' which 'e promises to present at ze next Festival.

Absinthe and I return to Five Station Approach to enjoy ze new ventriloquist show, a revival of *Bill and Ben*, ze flower-pot men, wizout subtitles.

Ze next day is Valentine's Day. Absinthe receives twenty bunches of red roses. She is disappointed to receive so few. But I am 'appy she 'as become so popular in Addlestone and can occupy 'er time wizout me.

March

March already! 'Ow time 'as flown – or 'Tempus Fuxit', as my Latin teacher used to say.

After ze Sunday service, ze verger, E. C. Surplice invites Absinthe and me to ze Coq au Vin wine bar for an apéritif.

'Call me Eric,' ze verger insists. 'D'yer know, Addlestone is steeped in 'istory. 'Ave you 'eard the story of Lady Jane Heriot?'

'No, Eric, I am still learning about Addlestone. Do tell me.'

Eric takes a sip from 'is glass of Entre Deux Merdes and a crisp from 'is packet of Jules Verne 'Mushy Peas Flavour'.

'Well, this Lady Jane fell in love wiv a commoner, called Nobby. 'Er father was very angry and accused 'im of rapin' 'is daughter, even though she was perfectly willin' every time. Nobby was sentenced to death and the execution by hangin' was set for six the next mornin'. In desperation, Lady Jane sent a fax to the King, who granted a reprieve and sent a despatch rider to Addlestone. Nobby was taken to the Execution Shoppin' Centre, and the execution was set for when the Free Range Church bell struck six. Unfortunately, the despatch rider stopped off at the Dog and Duck and didn't arrive at the hanging ground until five past six. But! – Lady Jane had strapped her legs round the clapper of the church bell and prevented it strikin' six. So the execution was delayed and the reprieve was received just in time to save Lady Jane's lover.

'Henceforth, Lady Jane was known as Ms Quasimodo, especially because she always liked the hump.' Eric winked.

'What a marvellous legend! Thank you, Eric. 'Ave another Deux Merdes.' What a mind-addling place Addlestone is!

Back in ze Dog and Duck in ze evening. We meet Kev and Rodge again.

'So yer went to the Free Range Church again, me old Froggie leg?'

'It was charming,' I respond. 'But I wish ze human members of

18

ze congregation would wear aftershave. Zey are higher zan ze animals.'

'Come off it, Ash tray,' Kev is offended, 'You Froggies are the kings of perfume. I've sniffed that Channel Number Nine in the streets of Paris. Be honest, Ash, I bet you miss nuffink from France.'

'Frankly, Kev,' I reply, 'you are right. Personally, I miss nothing. But, alas, Absinthe misses a lot. Especially ze tasty French letters. She 'ates ze English flavours, like "Baked Beans" and "Fish and Chips". She misses ze taste of "Pernod" and "Soixante-Neuf du Pape".'

Rodge pipes up, 'Can yer make it 'ere tomorrow lunchtime? Yer might 'ave a nice little surprise!'

'Of course, Rodge, it will be my pleasure.' Rodge and Kev wink in unison.

'Cosmic! See yer tomorrow,' Rodge smiles.

Absinthe and I retire to Five Station Approach to spend ze evening listening to Radio Addlestone. Ze famous *Bill and Ben, Flowerpot Men* show 'as just finished, and a new programme is being broadcast for ze first time. Because it is after ze 'watershed' time, Radio Addlestone is allowed to transmit ze world's first pornographic version of *Blind Date*, where ze contestants all appear nude and ze listeners 'ave to phone in zer votes. Zen afterwards, zey broadcast ze first programme for ze deaf and 'ard of 'earing, called *Listen wiz Mother-in-Law*. Ze announcer starts, 'Are you sitting uncomfortably? Zen I'll begin.' Zen ze mother-in-law tells ze tale of ze seven dwarfs who marry 'er daughter, Snow Black.

When Absinthe and I are in bed drinking our Ovalteenies, we 'ear ze national news. Ze Chancellor is very proud. Three million more workers 'ave been made unemployed and, as a result, inflation 'as dropped to a record low: minus 4 per cent. I know zis must be true, because everybody in Addlestone is returning ze shoddy goods zey 'ave bought to ze stores in ze High Street, so ze Retail Price Index is going backwards. What an achievement for ze Chancellor of ze Ex-checker!

No wonder ze former Great Britain is ze strongest economy in Europe. Reluctantly we turn out Radio Addlestone and fall asleep, tired but 'appy.

Next morning, ze sun rises over ze TV aerials and satellite dishes of Addlestone's romantic skyline. It is great to be alive. I cannot wait to know what surprise my peasant yobbos 'ave for me down ze Dog and Duck.

At midday I go down ze pub. To my amazement zer is a banner 'anging outside ze Dog and Duck which says 'Freedom for Mange-Tout'. Zey 'ave got my name right for first time!

Inside everybody is zer: Rodge ze Dodge, ze Brain, Andronicus, Rod ze 'Od, Wally Connall and, of course, Kev, resplendent wiz open shirt, revealing 'is 'sofa', 'is gold chains and four-letter tattoos.

'Welcome, Ash, me Froggie 'ero!' Kev shouts from ze bar, where six Gutterspews are lined up yearning for 'is eager mouth.

'What is 'appening, Kev?' I ask in bewilderment.

'Brain, over to you,' Kev gestures to Mr Damage.

Ze Brain 'as a coughing fit, takes a slurp of Gutterspew, clears 'is throat and begins.

'Ladies and gentlemen, I am time-honoured today, in the august presence of the notables . . .' 'E looks closer at ze piece of paper 'e is reading from. 'Sorry, folk. Can't read me own writin' – in the august presence of the *notables* of Addlestone, to welcome to this ancient village a Frenchie who 'as 'ad the courage and perspicaciousness to leave the Frog legs of 'is native land and come and settle in a far, far better place than I do now, to quote the poet. Monsieur Ash-heel Blancmange-Tout, on behalf of the citoyens of Addlestone, I 'ave the honour of bestowin' on you the Freedom of the Ancient Village of Addlestone.'

Everybody applauds while ze Brain 'as another coughing fit and fumbles in 'is pocket. 'E brings out a ribbon wiz a Gutterspew Ale beer mat attached and ties it round my neck, coughing cigarette ash in my face as 'e does it.

'You will notice, me old Frog Ash tray, that the ancient motto of Addlestone is inscribed on the beer mat: "For Ever Addled and Stoned", and the original Latin version: "Bevo ergo Sum".'

Kev shouts, 'Speech, Ash! Speech!'

I am not prepared so I ask for a quick Cornish Pastis first.

'Friends. Addlestonians and yobbos, lend me your ears – to quote another poet. I am proud and 'umble to receive zis 'onour, which I shall 'enceforth wear wiz pride. But, may I ask, are zer any benefits to zis honour? Will I get my Giro Cheque?'

Kev intercedes: 'No trouble, Ash. I'll fix it for yer!'

Ze Brain chips in: 'The Freedom of the Village of Addlestone confers very special privileges. You may now release wind whenever and wherever you wish, and you are not obliged to keep the code of silence. Secondly, you need not use the toilet if it is inconvenient. In other words, you are free to behave like any other Addlestonian. Congratulations!'

'Thank you, Brain.' I am overcome and ask for another Cornish Pastis.

'Now you've got the Addlestone Gong, Ash, you've gotta work for me.' Kev puts 'is 'and round my neck and reduces my oxygen supply again.

'What do you need, Kev?' I gasp.

'There's been a change in the Council election schedule. It was due at the end of the month. But, fortunately, the incumbent – known as the "bent income" to us voters – the "bent income" 'as died, which forces a by-election next week. Unfortunately, 'is snotty-nose BMW-drivin' son, the now 'Sir' Cedric Pumpkin-Smythe, will stand next week and try and take over the seat.'

'Because of 'is father's death, zat is why it is called a bye-bye-election?' I ask.

Kev ignores me and carries on: 'I need you, Ash, to endorse my European platform.'

'What is your manifesto, Kev?' I wait wiz battered breath.

'Simple, me overgrown tadpole. If my lot, the Addlestone Yobbocrat Party, gets elected, we'll transform the face of planet Addlestone. First, we're gonna lift the burden off the poor wiv double Giro Cheques every week. That'll sort you and me out for a start, eh Ash!' 'E gives me an 'efty nudge into ze Gents urinal once more.

'Then we'll extend Page Three of the *Addlestone Strumpet* to Page Five, Seven and Nine, to win the local macho vote.'

'But what do you mean about Europe, Kev?' I venture to ask.

'That's where you come in, mon matelot. We're gonna dyna-mite the Channel Tunnel to stop you Froggies streamin' over for our Giro Cheques. And then we'll close down the Rude Brothers swanky French restaurant. I rely on you, mon Ash tray, to convey the importance of this message to every doorstep in Addlestone. All right, me matelot mate?'

I spend ze week doorstepping for Kev and 'is Euro programme. It is very interesting. I learn many new four-letter words which are not tattooed on Kev. Kev thinks 'e 'as no chance to win against ze arrogant Cedric Pumpkin-Smythe, so 'e changes 'is name by deed poll to 'Kev Pumpkin-Smith'. Addlestonians cannot read, 'e says, so wiz 'is new name 'e 'as a fifty-fifty chance of ze voters putting a cross against 'is name.

'But aren't you afraid of your mother-in-law's Ad Lib Party?' I ask 'im after a couple of Gutterspews.

'Ash, me old Frog leg, my spies 'ave done a secret 'pinion poll. The only person who'll vote for 'em is me wife's grandad, 'cos 'e was married to a Lesbian for twenty-five years before realizin' it. But 'e still carries a torch for 'er – one of those electric ones wiv a big 'ead, yer know what I mean?'

When it comes to election day, ze turn-out at ze Dog and Duck is 100 per cent, but ze Polling Booth is very quiet. When ze results are declared at eleven-thirty on Thursday evening, in ze First Addlestone Brownie Pack Nissen Hut, ze returning officer reads out: 'Sir Cedric Pumpkin-Smythe, Addlestone Clobberam Party: 25. Mrs Strangelove, Ad Lib Separatist Party: 3, Kev Pumpkin-Smith: 26.'

Ze Nissen 'ut erupts into applause! What a victory for ze Giro Cheque classes! Kev takes us all to ze Dog and Duck to celebrate.

Next lunchtime, Kev comes round to Five Station Approach just as Absinthe and I are re-'eating ze delicious Tandoori take-away we couldn't finish ze night before because we 'ad celebrated Kev's victory wiz too much Gutterspew. I offer 'im a glass of pink Babycham to celebrate, but 'e refuses wiz a typical Addlestone grimace, leaning over wiz 'is mouth open and sticking out 'is *haute couture* fur tongue as far as 'e can. 'No Gutterspew by any chance, mon president?'

I serve 'im a can of Super Spew Extra Export with 9.2 per cent alcohol by volume. Zer is a warning label on ze can: 'For Export Only – Not To Be Consumed On Or Near The Streets Of Addlestone'. Apparently, ze Health and Safety Department of ze Runnynose Council insisted because zey found zey could not afford ze prices asked by ze newly privatized street-cleaning company.

'Cheers, mon president! I 'ave to thank yer for yer incredulous campaign effort which gave me such a landslide victory. I would now like to co-op you onto my new cabinet to 'elp me execute the citizens of Addlestone wiv my amazin' new reform programme.'

'E starts on 'is second Super Spew and expounds ze Yobbocrat plan of action. After ze success of ze Addlestone Rap Poetry Festival, 'is cabinet will proceed wiz ze Arts Festival next month, which will be combined wiz ze Addlestone All-Fringe Theatre Festival to save ze costs of advertising and washing-up ladies. Plans for ze world's first Karaoke Eurovision Song Contest are also well advanced: ze Addlestone First Brownie Pack Nissen Hut Hall 'as already been booked for ze Easter weekend and Councillor Kev kindly asks me to be joint TV presenter because I speak French and a word or two of Italian. Ze English presenter will be Sharon, ze daughter of Bruiser Reade, ze landlord of ze Dog and Duck. I 'ave seen 'er ze other day, getting out of 'er Greek boyfriend's Ferrari in ze High Street, apparently after an extended weekend in London. She is very voluptuous and known by ze locals as 'Girl Friday' because she was very friendly wiz Addlestone Friday football team until she met 'er Greek boyfriend, Costas Megalopolos. Absinthe frowns. I know why: Sharon always wears micro-skirts and blouses to match though she is not micro 'erself. I try 'ard not to show too much pleasure at ze invitation in front of Absinthe.

Kev, now on 'is fourth Super Spew, pauses for dramatic effect and another swig.

'But now, mon collaborator, the "coup de grace" – or, as we anglophobes say, the "lawnmower". "Coup de grace", lawn-mower – geddit?' 'E doubles up wiz guffaws and spills 'is beer. Absinthe and I laugh politely.

When 'e recovers and 'as taken another slurp, our noble councillor outlines 'is grand plan for Addlestone University. 'A millstone in the educational development of our people,' as 'e puts it.

It will be called ze Addlestone Open University because ze campus will be ze Dog and Duck car park every Wednesday evening, weather permitting. I am honoured to be invited to be ze University's first Emeritus Professor in French Studies.

'It was the Brain's idea, Ash. We 'ave to teach our students the rudements of Frog lingo before they disappear in their caravans to France for their summer 'olidays.' And zen, wiz great pride, Kev lifts 'is beer can 'igh and gives a toast: 'To our new Emeritus Prof, who well deserves the Addlestone Open University Folding Chair of French Studies!'

'E apologizes for it being only a Folding Chair, but explains ze tight budget and, in any case, it's easier to carry in when it rains.

'Ze other university 'facilities', as Kev puts it, will include Folding Chairs in Tattooolgy, very popular in zis part of ze country 'e tells me. Also 'is friend, Des Cart, will take ze Chair of 'Meteophysical' Philosophy and Andronicus, Winston Thatcher, 'as accepted ze Chair in Applied Rap Grafitti.

I 'ave to ask Kev what is Meteophysical Philosophy, because I do not understand. 'E explains to me.

'I'm not too sure, Professor Mange-Tout.' 'E 'as become very deferential to me all of a sudden. 'But the Brain tells me it means the futuristic study of whether it will 'appen tomorrow or whether it won't. A sort of philosophical astrology if yer like. Anyway, Des Cart 'as all the answers. 'E's a famous TV broadcaster and existentialist whose motto is "To Be Or Not To Be". Our rap prof, Andronicus, the Shakespearean expert is a great mate of 'is.'

It is Andronicus' birthday, which 'e celebrates in ze Coq au Vin wiz an amazing number of bottles of Chateau Plonqueur. It is a charming evening of wine slurping until, all of a sudden, disaster swoops! A lady in police uniform arrives in ze wine bar and accosts Winston Andronicus, who is already quite 'Titus'. She tells 'im 'e 'as committed a serious crime by delivering obscene rap poetry at ze Festival, so 'e must be arrested. Andronicus is 'bouche-frapped' and emotional because it is 'is birthday celebration. 'E protests zat 'e 'as not done anything wrong, not even when 'e went to ze Addlestone Friday football match wiz ze Friday Supporters Club at ze weekend.

But ze police woman refuses to listen. Instead, she uses a brilliant stroke of British police psychology. She takes all 'er uniform off and invites Andronicus to kiss 'er all over. Winston complies wiz 'er every wish and everybody applauds 'is technique and takes photographs wiz cameras which zey 'appen to 'ave wiz zem. I do not understand why zey all find zis terrible situation so funny and cannot stop laughing.

Finally, ze police lady puts all 'er clothes on again and, after a generous tip from ze Brain and Kev, she takes Winston out of ze wine bar, presumably to ze police station, where Winston turns out to spend ze night. 'E leaves wizout any fuss, in fact wiz a big smile on 'is face. Ze British bobbies are fantastique! I wonder if our French riot police, ze CRS, could be trained to use such sophisticated psychological techniques?

It is now ze end of March and ze Addlestone Open (Car Park) University 'as initiated a soon-to-be famous University Boat Race on ze Wey Navigation Canal against ze Open Night School University of Weybridge, which is situated in ze playground of ze Wham Bang Wallop College, where zer is plenty of lighting after dark. Ze race is between two dongolas which turn out to be like ze gondolas I 'ave seen in Venice but zey are each manned by ten men who propel ze dongola by standing facing forward. Using long paddles alternately one on either side of the boat.

Zer is intense rivalry between ze two universities. Both crews 'ave been working on zer boats and training for at least two wecks. Ze race takes place on ze canal from ze Addlestone Sewage Works to ze Weybridge Boathouse 'Otel, a distance of nearly two miles. Because zer are several locks along ze canal, ze object of ze race is for ze first dongola to reach each lock 'as ze right to go through first and keep ze boat behind waiting until zey 'ave cleared ze lock and ze water 'as regained its level.

When ze great day arrives, ze crews carry zer boats to ze canal edge. Ze Addlestone Open University is resplendent in slime green and puce tee shirts inscribed wiz ze slogan of zer sponsor: 'Ideal Standard Spring Water – Recycled like it Oughta'.

Ze Weybridge Open Night School crew is wearing luminous grey shirts wiz simply ze name of zer sponsor printed: 'St George's Hill United Arab Emirates Friendship Golf Club Ltd'.

Ze towpaths are lined wiz excited supporters: on ze right bank, ze St George Hillians, men dressed in boaters, blazers and white flannels wiz grey rosettes in zer buttonholes, women wearing large 'ats wiz fruit bowls on top and flimsy cotton dresses wiz Laura Ashley dock-leaf and dandelion prints; on ze left bank ze Addlestonians wiz slime green and puce scarves, men and women dressed alike in blue denim suits – ze only way to tell zem apart is zat ze girls do not 'ave pony tails, earrings or gold chains and zer tattoos are more delicate. Zer seems to be intense rivalry between ze two sides. Ze left bank shouts curses and abuse at ze other side – Kev pulls open 'is shirt even wider and points at ze four-letter words on 'is chest and stomach. Ze right bank shouts back 'Rah! rah! rah!' and 'St George's Hill is brill!'

Ze starter, Rod ze 'Od, examines ze boats to check everything is OK. 'E thinks 'e sees something wrong wiz ze rear of ze Weybridge boat but, after a quick feel under ze stern, 'e pronounces it fit and goes over to ze starting platform, an upturned crate of Gutterspew 10X. 'E tosses an empty beer bottle into ze canal and ze race is off! Both towpaths scream zer encouragement wildly, ze right bank waving zer golfing umbrellas and ze left bank waving beer cans.

Addlestone immediately moves into ze lead, paddling wildly, wiz Weybridge struggling already.

'*Fantastique!*' I shout to Kev, who comes over and speaks in my ear.

'Weybridge 'as no chance, Ash. Rod saw to zat when 'e "checked",' – 'e winks 'eavily – 'the stern of zer boat. Weybridge is towin' a two 'undred pound lead anchor.' 'E taps ze side of 'is 'ead and we all race down ze towpath after Addlestone, who reach ze first lock ten lengths ahead of Weybridge. Addlestone are into ze lock and 'ave closed ze entry gate before Weybridge arrives. Because ze race is upstream, Weybridge must wait for ze lock to empty again after Addlestone 'ave gone through: zis gains zem another ten lengths. Addlestone clears ze last two locks wiz ease and crosses ze finishing line to ze cheers of ze left bank, who 'ave kept pace wiz zem all ze way. A hundred yards behind on ze right bank, Weybridge supporters are rah-rahing zer 'ardest, but zer crew is beaten and very tired.

By ze time ze Weybridge boat 'as crossed ze line, Addlestone is already ensconced in ze Boathouse Hotel cocktail bar downing zer first pints. All except Rod, zat, is, who is wisely checking ze stern of ze Weybridge dongola again before it is lifted out of ze water by its shattered, gasping crew.

Ze St George's Hillians join us at ze bar and order gin and tonics. Ze Brain climbs onto a chair wiz difficulty and calls for silence as loudly as 'e can through 'is cigarette and coughs. 'E congratulates Addlestone on zer 'istoric victory, and also Rod for 'is 'unpeccable' refereeing of zis great sporting contest, which 'e 'opes will become an annual fixture. An enormous belch escapes from ze bar and ze St Hillians all glare at Kev, who smiles. 'Sorry, Mr Chairman. That's old Addlestonian for 'ear 'ear!'

Ze Brain introduces two dignitaries to present ze winner's prize: ze Lady Mayoress of Weybridge's Umbridge Borough

Council, festooned in a two-foot wide brimmed blue 'at and a blue-and-white sailor suit zat was a brilliant design for a six-year-old; and zen beside 'er steps up ze Lord Mayor of Runnynose Council, psychedelically dressed in a lime-green, double-breasted blazer, a scarlet cravat wiz purple tango dots, and, to bottom it all, pink flannels and blue canvas sailing slippers.

Ze Lady Mayoress says she is frightfully frightfully pleased to present Addlestone Open University wiz ze first Boat Race trophy, and Brian Damage 'ands 'er a large ten-pint cut-glass tankard which she proceeds to 'and to ze Addlestone skipper, 'Gold Top', our very own ginger-haired milkman, no less! Zer is watery applause from from ze St Hillians and loud shouts and whistles from ze Addlestone set. Gold Top grunts 'is thanks and lifts ze tankard 'igh for ze *Addlestone Strumpet* photographer.

We all order another drink and admire ze trophy. Ze glass is engraved wiz a very appropriate Latin motto: *Per Aqua Dux Ad Astra*.

Gold Top is ze 'ero of ze hour and several St Hillian young ladies take ze fancy to 'is bulging muscles which 'e is of course able to exercise every morning lifting 'is milk crates, though 'e does not mention zis to ze elegant creatures around 'im. Gold Top, 'imself, takes 'is fancy to one very attractive demoiselle – very scantily clad for ze time of year in a fur-trimmed micro skirt. She is Cynthia Brille-Laye, Goldie tells us when we adjourn back to ze Dog and Duck.

'She says she'll look over 'ere and meet me for a drink. 'Ow about that, then?' Goldie puffs out 'is sofa and twiddles 'is gold chain.

'Cor,' Kev chips in, 'that's a bit like crossin' the Berlin Wall for 'er lot, ain't it?'

'E turns to me and explains zat zer is a frontier post between Weybridge and Addlestone and ze parents insist on zer daughters 'aving special passes before crossing over to Addlestone because ze peasants 'ere aren't gentlemen and zer darling daughters might become HIV positive overnight.

'Anyway,' Goldie is not deterred, 'she says she's comin' over next Tuesday night. She's all of sixteen, she doesn't need to listen to mummy and daddy, I told 'er.'

Rodge bets 'im she 'as 'undreds of boyfriends so 'e doesn't stand ze chance of finding a virgin in a brothel.

I ask: 'Where is zis brothel wiz virgins, Rodge?'

After I replace ze pint zat Absinthe 'as just knocked out of my 'and to ze floor, Rodge explains it is just a local expression for an impossible situation. 'Ow vivid Addlestone English is!

Absinthe and I leave ze yobbos to zer crazy 'opes and dreams and Gutterspews, and go back to Five Station Approach wiz a Pol Pot Pourri fresh-meat take-away, just in time to 'ear ze Radio Addlestone late night news. Apparently, two super-yobbos from Addlestone went to ze famous Thrope Park amusement park, down ze road from 'ere, full of fifteen pints of Super Spew. As a result of zis, zey fell off ze Big Wheel fifty-five feet to ze ground. But, miraculously, zey both arrived on ze ground wiz only a few bruises. Zey are alive!

'Ron and I were totally relaxed thanks to Super Spew lager,' said 'is friend Jock in ze radio interview, 'so we 'ardly felt a thing. I'm lucky to be alive and everyone says it must be down to the beer. In future I'll stick to Super Spew.'

Following ze interview, Radio Addlestone broadcasts a very clever commercial: 'The more you do, with Super Spew brew, the safer for you!' We discover later zat it was our adman friend, J. Wally Connall, who 'ad ze brilliant idea to produce a radio commercial about zis event so quickly. Addlestone High Street really is ze Madison Avenue of Surrey! What a fantastique centre of culture!

Absinthe and I retire to bed, after a Cornish Pastis of course. I am not tired but Absinthe 'as a 'eadache'. I wonder if Rodge was telling ze truth about zer being no brothel in Addlestone? I must ask Kev tomorrow.

Brian Damage

April

It is April ze first, 'poisson d'avril'! I decide to play a joke on Councillor Pumpkin-Smith. Absinthe writes for me a notice saying 'OUT OF ORDER' which I plan to stick on ze Gents toilet at ze Dog and Duck so zat Kev will 'ave to use ze car park! But when we get to ze pub zer is a notice on ze entrance saying 'CLOSED FOR REDECORATION'. It is very disappointing, so we go down ze High Street to ze Coq au Vin and order a bottle of Addlestone's famous Veuve Twankey champagne to drink in ze new month. Ze barmaid, Marie, is very voluptuous and not too proud to 'ide it. She is called 'Celeste' because zey say she only goes down if she is carrying gold.

'It's early for you two to be in 'ere,' she raises 'er 'eavily painted eyebrows.

'We'd be in ze Dog and Duck normally, but its closed for repairs today, it says on ze notice outside,' I explain.

'You ain't fallen for that old gag 'ave yer?' Celeste laughs at me. 'They do it every year on April Fool's Day so's they can keep out the undesirables and drink in there on their own. Bruiser Reade and Kev always do it. You're an April fool, Ash mon ami! Yer can get in round the back.'

I am red wiz anger. My French blood will not allow me to be fooled by zees English peasants. We go back to Five Station Approach, where Absinthe writes a second 'OUT OF ORDER' sign so I can put one on ze Ladies toilet door as well so even ze ladies will 'ave to use ze car park.

We go round ze back of ze Dog and Duck and enter next to ze toilets, where I stick up ze OUT OF ORDER notices and zen stroll nonchalantly across to ze bar, where Kev, Rodge, Rod, ze Brain and Andronicus are obviously on zer umpteenth Gutterspew.

'Didn't yer see the sign outside, mon Froggie brave? This place is closed!' 'E guffaws loud enough to wake ze dead, or all of Addlestone, whichever are ze more lively.

29

'Don't try to nudge me today, Kev. Ze toilets are out of order. Look!'

'Cor, I 'adn't noticed that, Ash.' Kev turns to 'is wife, Mavis. 'Don't mind if I use the Ladies, Mave my little buttercup?'

'Mave' is anything but little; a woman of large proportions and radiant blonde hair – presumably ze reason for ze buttercup. I explain zat ze Ladies is out of order as well, while I wink at Sharon behind ze bar and she winks back.

'That's a bit rough, Mave, specially after all these Spews,' says Kev as panic sweeps ze faces of ze assembled throng like a winter Mistral. 'Nuffink for it, fellow Yobbocrats, we'll *all* 'ave to use the car park. Mave, you're not small, you'll 'ave to go behind the Bruiser's Range Rover.'

Zey all troop out ze back door to ze car park wiz a grim purpose. I shout after zem: 'Be careful not to pollute ze Open University campus!' But zey are all too preoccupied to acknowledge my funny joke. I go and take down ze 'out of order' notices and go back to my Gutterspew and laugh wiz Absinthe and Sharon until zey all come back in looking very much relieved.

'April Fools,' I shout in glee as zey come back to ze bar. 'It was I who put up ze "out of order" notices! It wasn't true at all. I just wanted you to exercise ze Freedom of Addlestone!'

Zey are very Victorian and not amused. Kev is indignant: 'D'you realize, me old Ash-face, that my Mavis might 'ave caught a nasty chill. She might even be HGV positive now.' And wiz zat zey all burst into laughter and 'e gives me ze biggest elbow nudge yet right across ze linoleum straight through ze Gents' door and a direct 'it right into ze urinal. I pick myself up and stagger back to ze bar.

Everybody is laughing, especially Absinthe, who cannot control 'erself and disappears into ze Ladies. Everybody offers me a Spew and congratulates me on my Gallic sense of 'umour. 'Didn't think you Froggies 'ad it in yer,' says Rod, scratching 'is sofa.

'Of course,' I reply, 'it's a French tradition as well. We call it "poisson d'avril".'

'What's that, Prof?' asks ze Brain, 'April poison?' And 'e 'as a laughing and coughing fit simultaneously, wizout losing 'is cigarette. We enjoy our Spews and laugh ze morning away, though my 'ands are frequently over Absinthe's ears as everybody tells many purple jokes. Absinthe scolds me, saying she 'as 'eard zem all many times before. I wonder where? Perhaps at ze Women's Institute where she goes twice a week?

Tomorrow is Sunday and Kev warns me not to go to ze Free Range Church because it is ze Feminist Festival. I tell 'im zat I cannot duck my devotions and Absinthe must not be disappointed. We say 'au revoir' and stagger back to Five Station Approach, tired but 'appy.

Next morning we are up early and go to ze church for ze nine-thirty Communion service. Trev ze Rev 'as introduced a new policy of accepting guest ales for ze communion ceremony and, because it is Feminist Sunday, zer is a guest lady preacher invited by ze Addlestone Liberation Front, ALF, or Ad Lib for short. We do not sing hymns for obvious reasons but we sing 'hyrrhs', which 'ave been specially written for ze feminist service from ze book of 'Hymns Ancient and Modern'. Absinthe sings wiz gusto 'The Lord is my Sheperdess, I Shall not Want' and 'Onward, Christian WRAC's'.

When it comes to ze lesson, ze guest preacher, ze Reverend Lesley Bian, reads ze story of Genesis from ze Revised Feminist Bible.

'And the Lady God created Woman in her own image. And she was sore amazed how beautiful was her creation. And the Lady God called her Eve because she always kept saying "At the end of the day". But because Eve was alone and desperate for a mate like all the creatures of the Earth, God caused a deep sleep to fall on Eve and took one of her three nipples, and out of it she did make a mate for Eve which was called Man Because he would put the woe into Wo-man; But at first Eve was sore delighted and sometimes just plain sore.

'Everything was paradise in the Garden of Eden and the Woman and the Man were allowed by Lady God to eat of every tree in the garden except the Fig Tree of Knowledge. The fig tree was heavy with fruit and the Man lusted after the figs of knowledge, but he was sore afraid of being nagged by Lady God. But Eve introduced him to the Serpentine Insurance Company salesman who seth: "Lady God doth know that in the day ye eat thereof of the Tree of Knowledge, then shall your eyes be opened and ye shall know the good and evil of the small print in the contract."

'So the Man picked of the Fig Tree of Knowledge and he

sucked the fig hard, because he wasn't getting on too well with Eve at the time. And he knew he was naked and liked it. But the Lady God was sore angry, and she banished Eve and the Man from the Garden of Eden into the wilderness of evil outside.

'And Lady God seth unto the Serpentine Insurance salesman: "Because thou hath corrupted the Woman and the Man, hence-forth, upon thy belly thou shalt crawl and dust shalt thou eat all the days of thy life". And the Lady God named him Lloyds. And the Man was glad to be in the wilderness: And the Woman was free to become the first single parent, and remove her fig leaf whenever a rich man came along. And they lived unhappily ever after. To this day insurance men crawl on their stomachs and men don't give a fig.

Here endeth the lesson.'

On ze way out of ze church I ask Trev ze Rev why zer were no animals at today's service. 'E explains zat it was enough to cater for ze feminists and, in any case, 'e didn't 'ave enough barrels of guest ale for communion.

Uplifted by zis spiritual experience, back at Five Station Approach Absinthe re-'eats a splendid Tandoori take-away, which we wash down wiz a bottle of Entre Deux Merdes – amaz-ingly on ze label ze vintage is next year. I wonder 'ow zey do it? Maybe ze vineyard 'as bought grape futures, or the labels are only printed every three years to save cost.

Our local dairy service is wonderful, something we do not 'ave in France. Fresh doorstep deliveries of milk every day and you can also order free-range eggs, fruit juices and yoghurts, even chickens. Our milkman, Gold Top, collects ze money every Saturday. One Saturday, when I am paying 'im, 'e announces important news.

'Monsieur Blancmange-Tout, I am very honoured to be able to tell you that our company, the Addlestone Independent Dairy Society – AIDS for short – is mountin' a big expansion programme. Soon we're gonna be distributing, not just in Addlestone, but all over Chertsey and even Weybridge! 'Course it'll mean expanding our float fleet, from two to six probably. And they'll 'ave to travel further and faster! So we've got the Wokin' milk-float electric engine factory designin' a new' – 'e pokes 'is finger into my Yves St Laurent night-shirt – 'a new *Formula One* V8 turbo model that'll go up to 17 miles an hour!'

'E steps back in amazement at 'is own statement. I try very 'ard to look appropriately 'bouche-frappé'.

'But that is not all, Monsieur Mange-Tout.' 'E puts 'is 'ead close to my ear, cupping 'is hands round 'is mouth, and whispers, 'We gonna expand our sales service as well, to include.' – 'E pauses dramatically to tickle my anticipation – 'To include deliveries of – condoms, should anyone so wish.' 'E winks surreptitiously. 'Of course they'll be left on the doorstep in plain wrappers. And you can 'ave any flavour your missus likes.'

I foolishly suggest to Goldie zat it is perhaps a little late in ze night, at seven in ze morning, to deliver condoms of whatever flavour. Goldie points out my stupidity by explaining zat zees are specially formulated 'breakfast condoms' with appropriate flavours: fruit juices various, muesli, yoghurt and All-Bran. I call it "Breakfast in Bed",' 'e beams, and steps back giving me ze longest wink I 'ave seen in Addlestone so far.

'Finally,' 'e announces, 'we must of course 'ave a new advertising slogan, which is: FROM CONTENTED COWS TO CONTENTED CUSTOMERS – WE KNOW HOW TO MILK 'EM.' And wiz zat 'e gives me ze milkman's salute, disappears into 'is shortly-to-be obsolete milk float and whirrs off down Station Approach. Ze tradesmen in Addlestone never cease to amaze me. I go in and ask Absinthe what she likes for breakfast.

Later, on Saturday afternoon, we go to our first British football match at ze Addlestone Friday FC ground. Zey are playing ze famous local team, Chertsey Pathetic, who 'ave ze distinction, Wally Connall tells me, of being ze only team in ze area to 'ave reached ze qualifying rounds for ze national Fifth Division. Wally 'as kindly invited us into ze directors' box because 'e is ze club's chairman. Ze directors' box only 'olds six people standing, but zer are shelves for many lager cans. Unfortunately, it is raining 'pussies and puppies', and ze roof of ze box is leaking all over us. Wally's wife is wiz us, resplendent in 'er nylon leopard-skin trouser suit complete wiz plastic rain hat, and just as Wally opens ze first can of lager Kev appears wiz Mave.

Ze teams trot out onto ze pitch, which is two thirds under water, and ze capacity crowd of at least forty people raise a '10X' cheer. Ze crowd is split into two groups in cages at opposite ends of ze pitch, to avoid trouble between ze rival supporters.

Wally pulls a face 'It's a cryin' shame we can't afford to rent any hooligans to beat up the visitors. We could do with the publicity. It's the only way we could get national recognition, 'cos it won't happen with the football we play, that's a cast iron certainty.'

Chertsey, because of zer success, carry sponsorship on zer shirts: 'Germbusters'. I ask Wally what it means.

'In fact, it's an Addlestone company, but they wouldn't touch Addlestone Friday with a gondola paddle. Germbusters was the first organization in the county to set up a cleaning and fumigation service for the wheely-bins when the Runnynose Council introduced them and made them obligatorial.' I furrow my brow in puzzlement at ze word 'wheely-bin'. 'You know, Monsieur Ash, those plastic bins on wheels you put your rubbish in, and that get wheeled to the dustcart once a week by the Council. Made a fortune, Germbusters have. Operate all over the area now. Only they are rich and daft enough to support Chertsey Pathetic.'

I notice zat Addlestone also 'ave a slogan on zer backs:

TGIF
PHONE 5643
during opening hours

Wally explains 'Thank Goodness It's Friday' and says they 'ave no 'ope of sponsorship. 'They did have one offer recently, though, but I turned it down. The Addlestone Independent Dairy Society wanted to put on: "AIDS, Delivered fast and fresh."'

Ze whistle blows and ze game is off. Wally and Kev scream abuse at Addlestone as Chertsey score twelve times in ze first ten minutes, including seven penalties because ze Addlestone defenders all use zer 'ands to try to keep ze ball out of ze goal. It seems ze object of ze game is to put ze ball in ze opponent's net so zat ze scorers can run round ze pitch for ten minutes, jumping up and down, punching ze air and wrapping zer legs round each other. I remark on zis to Wally and Kev in between tirades of swearing.

'It's obligatorial, Ash. You see number three? That's Nobby Pyles. 'E's our striker. The only 'alf-decent player we've got. Nearly got selected as an international: 'e could score all right, but 'e failed the ballet lessons. Couldn't jump high enough to get 'is legs round their necks – always ended up booting them in the groin. So they couldn't select him. Pity really. 'E's a good scorer when 'e's not playing with this bunch of arseholes.'

Finally, after a freezing ninety minutes watching ze teams splashing through ze mud and water holes, indistinguishable from each other, covered from 'ead to boot in brown slime, we hear ze final whistle blow. Chertsey 'as won by forty-six goals to nil, an amazing tribute to Addlestone's unorthodox defence, Wally tells me, because only thirty of ze goals 'ave been penalties, and in any case Addlestone forced zer way into ze Chertsey half on at least two occasions, thanks to fouls. Ze Chertsey players do a tour of honour round ze pitch, carrying each other piggy-back to ze touchline and kneeling in ze mud shouting obscenities at ze directors' box. What a wonderful British sporting experience!

Wet and freezing, we all retire in Wally's 1958 Volvo to ze Coq au Vin. It is far too dangerous, 'e tells me, to risk ze Dog and Duck after a football match, especially wiz today's result. Marie Celeste serves us all nicely warm 10X Spew Lager. For ze first time I notice ze subtle Grunge Deco interior design of ze wine bar. Ze walls are quaintly decorated wiz corroded metal advertising signs for once-famous petrol and cigarette products, pet food and bird-seed brands. One sign says 'Join the Royal Navy – Increase Your Pay and Serve Your Country'. Margaret Thatcher must 'ave admired zis priority of duties before she privatized ze Royal Navy and sold ze fleet to ze Japanese. Zer is also 'Mobilgrease Special Grade for every part of your chassis – only available in Soho', as well as 'Rolling Rock Premium Imported Beer, 1939', clearly a forerunner of ze rock 'n' roll era.

Suddenly, when we are on our sixth 10X Spew, in walks Gold's girlfriend from ze Boat Race, Cynthia Brille-Laye from Weybridge. She is dressed immaculately in a low-cut bra-less see-through blouse and ultra-micro skirt. She looks radiant, including 'er face, but she is not wiz Gold, nor is she alone. 'Er escort is a slim young man wearing blue jeans wiz a white blazer and dark blue cravat; 'e 'as a small chin, protruding teeth and shaggy ginger hair. 'E is frightfully self-confident and leans on a large, red, white and blue striped golfing parasol.

Miss Brille-Laye introduces 'erself and ze young man to us, because she recognizes Kev, from ze famous belch at ze Boat 'Ouse after ze Boat Race. 'Please meet my friend, Nigel Fortescue-Weathercock, Bart; he's a St Hillian too.'

'How frightfully frightful to meet you all.' Ze words come from ze back of 'is throat as 'e 'olds out a dangling 'and for us to shake.

'Enchanted to meet you, Nige Bart. I may call you Nige, Mr Bart?' Kev raises a polite eyebrow. 'And smashin' to see you again, Cynf. May I make so bold, is this just a fleetin' visit to our shores in Addlestone?'

'Cynf' explains zat 'er parents did not go away for ze weekend, so she and Mr Bart 'ave booked into ze master suite at ze Dog and Duck for ze astronomical sum of twenty-five pounds a night, incidentally, just to enjoy ze local rustic charm of Addlestone, of course. Cynf explains zey are both recently engaged and we congratulate zem warmly. Nige orders four bottles of Veuve Twankey Addlestone champagne which we all drink wizout glasses in ze trendy Addlestone style; 'by ze throat' as zey call it.

Cynf and Nige bid farewell and retire to ze Dog and Duck. I tell Wally and Kev I found it very difficult to understand what Mr Weathercock was saying.

''E can't 'elp it. Froggie mate,' Kev explains. ''E was born wiv a toffee nose in 'is mouth. Brought up in Rotweiler country. Eton and Balliol – effortless inferiority. Can't articulate 'Er Maj's English wiv that background. Mind you, wiv a christian name like Wivacock, Cynf should be all right tonight!' 'E explodes wiz laughter and gives me one of 'is best nudges. Unfortunately ze Coq au Vin Gents is not in ze right place and I go flying into ze far wall, painfully dislodging an old metal advertisement for Liverpool Ferries which says, 'Go Abroad to the Isle of Man', together wiz another one showing a man riding a big jar in ze sea saying 'Bovril Prevents That Stinking Feeling'. I pick ze signs up and apologize to Marie Celeste behind ze bar.

''Pas de' problem, ducky! Or should I say 'mon petit canard'?' She gives me 'er naughty smile and 'er famous up-from-undies look.

Wally offers us another drink, but ze combination of Gutterspew lager and Addlestone champagne makes me yearn even for ze 'orrible English toilet facilities we 'ave at Five Station Approach. I didn't like to tell Kev when 'e quizzed us before, zat we miss, more zan anything else, our Provencal Turkish toilet and hot-water bidet. Absinthe and I bid zem 'bonne nuit' and race back to Station Approach just in time!

Over our Cornish Pastis nightcap, Absinthe and I exchange sorrow for Gold, who will obviously never 'ave ze voluptuous Cynthia Brille-Laye for 'is girlfriend. We watch ze weather forecast on TV, which promises an end to ze rain and a sunny day tomorrow, and retire to bed to ze romantic and refreshing sound of Addlestone rain pitter-pattering against our window pane as ze wind whistles musically down ze bedroom chimney.

We go to sleep tired but 'appy. Tomorrow is another day in Addlestone – what more could zer be to live for?

Suddenly, in ze middle of ze night, I am awakened by an 'uge crash outside. Ze wind is 'owling and ze rain beating fiercely on ze window pane. It is our first British 'urricane. 'Ow exciting! Absinthe is still snoring deeply, as usual after three pastis night-caps. I switch on ze light and see zat water is dripping from ze ceiling into 'er open mouth. I'm always telling 'er to take more water wiz 'er pastis! Maybe zis is ze answer! I use all my force to shake 'er into consciousness, as ze storm rages magnificently outside.

Absinthe is very upset to be woken up: 'I was 'aving a lovely dream about ze fountains at Versailles, which were spraying gallons of water into my mouth, but it was not ze usual Paris sewage smell – ze water was flavoured wiz Pastis 51 plus 18. It was marvellous and you spoiled it.' Finally she realizes what is 'appening, and she gets a large bucket to put on ze bed and catch ze water. Looking through ze window we see, during ze lightning flashes, zat ze crash was caused by a tree in ze next yard which 'as snapped in ze gale and fallen across ze roof of our cottage.

It is four fifteen in ze morning but I phone Kev for 'elp. 'Don't worry, Ash. I'll get Rod and 'is boys to come over and 'ave a look at first light. Just move the bed and keep the bucket under the leak. See yer in the morning.'

We could not move ze bed because ze room is too small, so we put ze bucket between us on ze bed and take it in turns to empty it and doze between symphonic crashes of ze 'urricane.

Kev and Rod's idea of 'first light' is ten-thirty. Absinthe and I 'ave emptied more zan one hundred bucketfuls of leaking water. 'Sorry, Ash mate. Didn't wake up till late. All those Spews last night. Slept right through the storm, would you believe? Anyway, we're 'ere. Let's take a look at the damage? Good weather for frogs, though!' 'E and Rod guffaw uncontrollably as we walk through to ze back yard.

Kev and Rod spend a long time looking at ze tree from next door, which is leaning against our chimney at a terrifying angle, wiz one branch poking through a nasty 'ole in ze tiles. Zer is a lot of lip-sucking and grim glance exchanges between Rod and Kev, and lots of 'Cor, that'll be expensive' mutterings. Zey go in up to ze attic and check ze 'ole from inside. 'It's like the Amazon jungle in their wiv all that foliage,' Rod says as 'e clambers down ze attic ladder.

''Ow quickly can you fix it, Rod?' I ask in trepidation. 'E explains zat first ze tree amputators 'ave to cut ze trunk and lift it away, but they're so busy after ze storm maybe zey can't do it until tomorrow, but 'e will arrange it for me. After zat 'e and 'is team of experts can get to work and repair ze roof.

'But also, mon brave, that chimney looks a bit crooked. Could kill somebody in the street if it fell over. I fink we 'ave to strap it up straightaway. It's a public 'ealth 'azard like that.' I can see Rod is warming to ze size of ze job. I tell 'im to arrange everything as quickly as 'e can.

'Shouldn't sleep there tonight though, Monsieur Ash.' Rod shakes 'is 'ead grimly. 'Not safe. I'll try to put some plastic sheeting over the 'ole today for damage limitation purposes, but you'll 'ave to spend the night somewhere else till the tree's gone.' Absinthe and I are desperate, but Kev takes us to ze pub and introduces us to 'Stevie Wonder', who 'as a barge wiz spare berths down ze canal. I ask Stevie 'ow much it will cost for Absinthe and I to spend a night on 'is luxury barge. Stevie is very kind and only asks fifty pounds per 'ead and six litres of cider. I realize zat Stevie is a wily old 'oiseau', so I bargain wiz 'im. Very reluctantly 'e reduces ze price to forty-eight pounds a head and five litres of cider. We shake 'ands and collect our night things from ze cottage. Stevie takes us down ze canal in 'is vintage Ital Marina.

We arrive at ze Addlestone lock, where Stevie parks ze car and helps us with our luggage across a little bridge and along ze towpath. Ze lock 'as not been used for years, Stevie tells us, which accounts for ze rotting green slime and fungus floating on ze water. We arrive at Stevie's barge; it is called ze *Spirit of Free Inebriation*. Stevie 'elps us to clamber over ze bows. Inside ze barge it is all wooden and quaint and very narrow. In ze living area, which is also ze kitchen and bar, there is an antique iron stove for burning logs and old copies of ze *Sun* and *Sunday Sport*. Steve shows us to our berths which are even narrower and covered in faded cushions. How Dickensian, I think!

Stevie kindly offers us a whisky from ze bar, which amazingly 'as a real optic to dispense it, 'ence ze name of ze barge. Stevie explains zat unfortunately it leaks, so 'e 'as to put a glass under it, which requires constant emptying via 'is mouth, or alternatively, 'e 'as to lie under it to catch ze drops, but usually 'e ends up falling asleep. 'E makes us all a magnifique spaghetti polonaise, wiz 'dancing pasta', according to ze label on ze can. Zer is no dining table, so we stand and eat on ze ledge by ze window. As I am eating mine, a spider comes down on 'is thread from ze ceiling and hovers two inches above my spaghetti. I jump back in 'orror.

'Don't worry, Ash mate. 'E's a friend of mine. I call 'im Spunky Spider. Just give 'im a little nibble and 'e'll go straight back up to 'is nest. 'E absolutely adores spag polonaise.'

I offer Spunky a small strand, which 'e grabs between 'is jaws, then 'e races up 'is web to ze ceiling, apparently contented.

After dinner, Stevie attacks ze cider wiz all ze ferocity of a beached whale. Several litres later, after Stevie 'as converted Absinthe and I to ze Addlestonian Socialist school, and I 'ave converted 'im to ze Exchange Rate Mechanism, Stevie says 'e is honoured to 'ave Common Market mates staying on 'is barge, and as a special privilege we can take turns to lie under ze whisky optic and drink ze drops, which we do until we are all very tired at four in ze morning, and retire to berth, tired but 'appy.

Next morning early, at ten o'clock English time, Stevie phones Rod, who tells 'im that ze tree will be removed during ze day and zat 'e will place a plastic cover over ze roof hole so that we can return to our idyllic cottage in Station Approach and sleep zer tonight. We thank Stevie for 'is generous 'ospitality and ze company of 'is friendly Spunky Spider and go back to Station Approach, where Rod tells us ze roof is now protected by a plastic sheet. 'Owever, 'e must find ze materials to repair ze roof, which may take a day or two, but not to worry, 'e'll sort it out for us. We return to Station Approach and sleep, tired but 'appy in ze knowledge zat ze roof will be repaired very soon.

MAY

Ze May blossom 'as started to come out between ze cracks in ze paving stones in front of Five Station Approach. Our window box is bursting wiz dandelions and ze flashers are out in ze park. 'Ow beautiful, ze British Spring!

It is now three weeks since ze big storm, and Rod and 'is team 'ave still not appeared to repair ze roof and chimney. Ze plastic cover 'e put over ze hole is only partially effective, so Absinthe and I still sleep wiz ze bucket on ze bed between us, which puts certain constraints on our sex life. Absinthe gets upset when she wakes up to find me making love to ze bucket. Quite frankly, after a few Cornish Pastis nightcaps, it is sometimes difficult to tell ze difference.

But zis is ze week of ze Addlestone Art Festival, organized by Brian Damage and Winston Thatcher. I 'ave been co-opted to mount ze painting exhibition in ze Addlestone First Brownie Pack Nissen Hut Hall. Ze local artists 'ave contributed an amazing range of works. I like best a painting of sunflower-oil bottles on Sainsbury's shelf by ze local postman, Vince ze Van, who is deaf in one ear and is a master of ze Addlestone Recessionist School. 'E could not afford ze trip to France to paint ze original sunflowers but, being a Recessionist, 'e made a virtue out of necessity and sat for hours in front of ze shelf at Sainsbury's.

Zer is also a portrait of ze barmaid at ze Coach and Horses, Lisa, entitled 'The Moaner' because she never smiles. Finally, I select another great work from ze Recessionist School, 'Nude on a Milk Float', painted by Goldie, our very own milkman, during 'is blue-top period.

But ze centrepiece of ze exhibition is a twenty-foot high sculpture composed of Polo Mints stuck together, entitled 'A Tribute to Henry Moore'. 'Owever, nothing can beat ze ginormous sculpture straddling ze traffic lights, ze 'Colossus of Roads' made out of pitta bread by ze local Greek restaurant waiter, Pheidias Xenophobos. Many old ladies are shocked by ze statue's proportions, and zer are angry letters in ze *Addlestone*

Strumpet to which I 'ave to reply zat art knows no boundaries, and in any case, I point out, it is dangerous if old ladies look skyward and don't keep zer eyes on ze ground while crossing at ze traffic lights.

A late entry is a strange work by Kev's mother-in-law. It is simply a wheely-bin wiz an arrow pointing to ze lid. Under ze arrow is written ze legend 'For Men'. Kev explains to me zat 'is mother-in-law and wife originally wanted to use a toilet bowl, but realized it was too small to accept ze male torso.

In honour of ze Festival, ze Dog and Duck 'as 'ired a jazz band consisting of white-haired veterans called ze Zimmerframe Dooh-Daah Band. Zey 'ave a saxophonist, a drummer, a double bass and a pianist, and zey are very good when zey find ze tune, which zey usually do once in every number, however fleetingly. Neverzeless, ze music is quite catchy and ze bald heads and blue rinses bob in rhythm to ze melodies. Ze band is lead by ze saxophonist, who gives witty introductions to each number, looks permanently hung over and swigs 'is ale and puffs furiously at 'is rolled cigarette on every possible occasion during numbers when 'e is not actually playing. Ze band leader, Cedric, is a friend of Kev, who 'as naughtily briefed 'im zat zer is a French couple in ze audience, so, at ze end of ze first session, Cedric proudly announces: 'In honour of our new Froggie residents, the Zimmerframes will round out this session with a well-known little French number dedicated to the "Chanel" Tunnel. Ladies and gentlemen, we give you the Frogs' national anthem in three four time – "La Mayonnaise"!'

Absinthe and I jump to attention. Ze first few bars are almost recognizable, but zen Zimmerframe jazz creativity takes over and ze melody is lost for ever. Neverzeless, we applaud politely at ze finish when ze Zimmerframes run out of notes and make desperate lunges for zer pints.

During ze interval I collar Rod ze Hod, who 'as still not brought 'is 'team' to fix ze roof. 'E says 'e 'as been very busy wiz many emergencies since ze storm, but promises to start wizin a couple of days. I ask Councillor Kev, who is standing next to us wiz 'is seventh pint of Gutterspew, why on earth ze TV weather forecast couldn't tell us about ze arrival of ze hurricane.

'Easy, my moustachioed tadpole, let me tell you the facts of life. Now I've become a member of the political establishment, I have insight into the machinations of our noble secret services.'

Kev puts an iron grip on my biceps, cutting off all circulation to my lower arm, and breathes Gutterspew fumes into my ear. 'Whenever there's a national emergency it's vital to keep panic off the streets, so the Min of Defence, which controls the Met office, always keeps an impending disaster hush-hush. After all, it wouldn't do if all the motorways got jammed by a panic-stricken populace, would it? The Queen and her noble ministers might never get to Heathrow in time and catch the first flight out to safety. Of course, a hurricane isn't as desperate as a nuclear attack, but the principle is still the same.'

'Really, Kev?' I am astounded. 'But at least the Cold War is over?'

'Not on your Frog nellie, Ash mate. It's all a myth invented by the Yanks to save defence expenditure and get the West out of the slump that our lot still laughingly call "recession". The Russians still have the largest arsenal of nukes in the world. And they're not even controlled by Moscow any more, but by a bunch of Ukrainian hick farmers who keep squirting out lethal leaks from their nuclear reactors every time they nod off on the job. How d'you think they can ever keep control of their missiles? No chance! It only needs one night watchman to trip over his bottle of vodka and land on the red button and whoosh! It's four-minute warning time over here and the politicians are racing for their bunkers and phoning their Swiss bankers, and we're still watching *Neighbours* totally oblivious, thank you very much, waiting for the blinding flash.'

I am completely 'bouche-frappé' by such a powerful speech, the like of which I 'ave not heard on ze British television or radio. 'Kev, wiz ideas like zat you could stand for Parliament! You would make Ken Livingstone and Derek Hatton seem like Margaret Thatcher. I didn't realize you were part of ze British intelligentsia. You should write a column in ze *Sun*.'

'You've only heard the tip of the iceberg lettuce, Ash-frog. If I had my way, we'd all be equal lager louts together, including the Royals. No more Addlestone champagne for the toffs – just Gutterspew 10X Lager for everyone. That's what I call democracy.'

'Kev, you are indeed very clever,' I exclaim, 'but could you or Rod bend your intellects to 'elping my sanitary arrangements at Five Station Approach? I am not criticizing English 'ygiene technology, especially in ze Dog and Duck of course, which I experience frequently. But at our cottage in Station Approach, Absinthe and I sorely miss our French toilet facilities. Could you or Rod arrange to supply us wiz a Turkish loo and bidet?'

Kev's eyes light up 'B-Day? Isn't that what we had in World War Two – the dress rehearsal two days before D-Day?' 'E guffaws and nudges my still – numb arm wiz enough force to deliver me on ze usual track into ze Gents urinal. I struggle to my feet and stagger back to ze bar, and tell Rod I am fundamentally serious. Maybe it could be worth 'is while to install a 'B-Day' and Turkish toilet at ze same time as repairing ze roof and water damage in ze attic. 'E assures me zer is no problem. But I insist on ze colour of ze porcelain. It must be traditional French marron glacé. Very important because it needs less cleaning. Again Rod promises to come round in a couple of days.

Trinity term 'as just begun at ze Addlestone Open University, and ze weather is brightening up enough for us to put our deck chairs out in ze car park. My first Wednesday lecture introduces ze students to ze basics of French language to help zem get by when zey go on zer camping 'olidays in boring Provence. I teach zem some phrases vital for survival:–

Donnez-moi une fracture, miel: Give me a break, honey.
Assez blonde, rayon de soleil: Fair enough, sunshine.
Hors de combat: Ze soldier's girlfriend.
Elle chez moi: 'Er indoors.
Menu à la carte: Meals on wheels.
Le weekend: I 'ave a touch of ze diarrhoea.
Cri de coeur: Ze dog is barking.
Lèse Majesté: Ze Queen 'as stayed in bed all morning.
Général de Gaulle: Ze goal-keeper.
Merde alors: Ze mother of ze European Commission President,
    Jacques Delors.
Tarte aux pommes: An Aussi Sheila wiz Englishmen.
Coup de grâce: A lawnmower.
Dans vôtre cul-de-sac: Innuendo.
Merde: Ze postilion 'as been struck by lightning!
Coq au vin: I'm sorry, mam'selle, I 'ave ze brewer's droop.

Ze lecture is cut short by a sudden downpour. We all fold up our deck chairs and race into ze Dog and Duck for a few Spews. Ze landlord, Bruiser Reade, is, surprisingly, behind ze bar for ze first time in weeks. 'E asks me 'ow ze lecture went, and I tell 'im if ze students can last ze course, zey should have no problems on ze bottomless beaches of St Tropez. Everyone is amazed to see Bruiser at 'is post, because it is traditional in Addlestone zat ze landlord is never seen. Ze local game is 'Spot ze Landlord', because normally zey are always out playing golf, sea fishing, at ze races or playing roulette in London. Whoever spots ze landlord first can take a free drink out of ze kitty, which ze customers contribute to. Bruiser is not behind ze bar for long, 'e 'as an urgent appointment at ze Champagne Bar at Ascot.

Absinthe 'as received a letter from 'er Italian cousin, Al Dente. 'E wants to come and visit us, because Absinthe 'as foolishly told 'im 'ow idyllic Addlestone is, and 'e is fed up wiz Bellagio, where 'e lives – a little village on ze shores of Lake Como, within sight of the Italian Alps. Al and 'is wife, Tortellina, are driving over from Italy and are expected zis evening, so I race back to Five Station Approach to 'elp get things ready.

Absinthe is preparing a typical English banquet: she is defrosting some Walls pork pies, and 'as ordered Spaghetti Polonaise and chips from ze Cloaca Maxima as a special Italian treat for our guests. I bring back some pink Babycham from ze off-licence and a crate of Tesco's best Italian own-label 'Fontanafred Paralitico, Vino da Lavatrice' (14 per cent alcohol), ze perfect complement to pork pies, chips and defrosted sliced bread topped wiz ketchup and mayonnaise. I suggest to Absinthe zat maybe we 'ave gone over ze top and could be encouraging ze Dente's to settle in Addlestone; ze last thing I want is to be crowded by Continentals coming to live in Addlestone and spoiling our rustic tranquillity. Absinthe will 'ave nothing of zis. It is her family and zey must be given ze 'tapis rouge' treatment.

It is nine-thirty and we are on our second bottle of Fontanafred Paralitico. Ze Dente's were supposed to arrive from Dover at seven o'clock. No chance wiz ze Italians, I think to myself, without daring to voice it to Absinthe.

Suddenly, zer is an engine roar at ze end of Station Approach, which becomes deafening as it gets closer, accompanied by ghetto-blasting radio music. It stops outside our front door. Al Dente and Tortellina 'ave arrived in zer gleaming red drop-head Dino Ferrari. Al vaults out of ze driver's seat wizout opening ze car door or turning off ze blaring radio. 'E races to our front door, where 'e gives Absinthe several kisses on each cheek, squeezing 'er shoulders fiercely. Tortellina sidles elegantly out of ze Ferrari by opening 'er door first, and walks towards us wiz lots of 'ip movement.

I 'ave not met Absinthe's charming cousins before, nor am I familiar wiz Italian extravaganza habits. Al is quite tall for 'is countrymen, about five foot three, wiz thick, curly black hair, eyebrows and moustache to match. 'E is elegantly dressed in an immaculate Valentino sweater, sharply pressed Fiorucci slacks, Gherardini shoes and ze obligatory Gucci handbag. 'Is after-shave is obviously a round-ze-clock Versace formula, which still fails to hide ze Italian garlic.

Tortellina is 'autre chose'. Raven 'air clipped back in a pony-tail, long black eyelashes, thick gold lipstick, wiz matching finger and toe nails, a low-cut, sleeveless beige blouse, short, turned-up khaki culottes and white patent leather sandals. She wears an abundance of gold bracelets and necklaces zat will be ze envy of all ze men in Addlestone, and carries an enormous stone-studded ring, which spans two fingers of her left hand. Apart from zat she is very pretty. I am beginning to understand where Absinthe's family gets its flamboyant tempers from.

Al, when 'e 'as finally finished rubbing 'is moustache all over both Absinthe's cheeks, bursts out wiz excitement: 'How fantas-tico to be 'ere in Addlastona. What a beautiful-a place-a to live! You are so lucky! Let-a me introduce-a my beautiful wife, Torta. It's-a short for Tortellina and means "little tart", you know.' Al gives me an embrace zat would make even a Provençal Frenchman suffocate. Torta 'ugs and kisses Absinthe, zen demurely gives me a light kiss on one cheek, but I notice ze kiss is really in 'er eyes. We go in and celebrate wiz drinks and pork pies. After six bottles of exquisite Vino da Lavatrice, and our wonderful English banquet, Al goes out to 'is Ferrari to collect 'is luggage and turn off ze car radio, which 'as been entertaining us for ze past two hours. Over Cornish Pastis we chat about ze problems of our tumultuous world: ze price of wine, ze quality of bread and ze cost of maintaining Ferraris in Italy.

We turn on ze television news, because Absinthe's cousins only see housewives stripping on Italian TV. But after watching ze massacres in Eastern Europe and Asia, ze famines in Africa, interviews wiz politicians telling us ze recession ended three years ago and ze British Queen closing another factory (she 'as nothing to open any more), we switch over to Radio Addlestone and listen to Jerry Logan's *Goodnight Addlestone* show. 'E 'as fantastic guests tonight: ze 'Pelmanist Duo' – zey are very clever, because ze girlfriend goes among ze radio audience and is given different objects from zer pockets, which 'er boyfriend, who is blindfolded, 'as to identify by telepathy. Ze lady asks 'im questions and miraculously 'e guesses exactly what ze object is every time wizout removing 'is blindfold. We do not 'ave zis creative use of radio in France.

Immediately after ze Pelmanists zey 'ave *Paws for Thought*, a special religious programme for 'ousehold pets, including budgies and goldfish, to 'elp zem wiz zer psychological and sexual problems. Al seems quite inspired by ze message and eager to go to bed, so we all retire.

I am tired but 'appy to dream of ze beautiful Torta. Ze bucket is still in ze bed between Absinthe and I, catching drops of water. I wish ze bucket was more cuddly. Maybe if I put a 'ot-water bottle inside it every night . . .?

Absinthe and I sleep late and ze bucket overflows onto ze bed, waking us up to an unusually sunny day. We all 'ave breakfast in our cosy concrete back yard, wiz reconstituted muesli and dried prunes, accompanied by specially preserved World War Two powdered egg, from which Absinthe makes an authentic 1940s dish of scrambled eggs (so popular wiz ze Spitfire pilots, I am told). Unfortunately zer is no powdered milk to mix wiz zem so we 'ave to use fresh Addlestone Independent Dairy Society milk, which Goldie managed to deliver only forty-eight hours after its sell-by date. We wash down zis delicious meal wiz new improved Horlicks 'au lait' (a special new breakfast formula to help Addlestonians sleep through ze day), and a glass of Cornish Pastis diluted wiz Sainsbury's '57 Varieties Exotic Fruit Juice'.

Al is ecstatic: 'What a wonderful-a life you have here in rural Addlastona! I cannot wait to buy a little-a farmhouse here wiz maybe a few acres of tarmac for my friends to park-a their Ferrari's!'

My heart sinks. I try to deter 'im by telling 'im ze price of property in Addlestone is rocketing, but Al is not deterred. 'E 'as made a fortune out of selling 'Signor Woppy' ice-cream from ze boot of 'is Ferrari around Lake Como so, unfortunately, ze lira is no object. 'E asks me to take 'im to ze local estate agent, but I try to divert 'im by suggesting a guided tour of ze sights of Addlestone before 'e makes up 'is mind. Al agrees and Torta gives me an encouraging look from 'er beautiful, mascara'd hazelnut eyes.

We visit ze imposing Safeways car park piazza, ze police station designed by ze local Cubist school of architecture, ze historic 1950s council flat tower block in Station Boulevard and, of course, ze Runnynose Council Social Security offices, where we all wave through ze windows and smile sweetly in ze 'ope my Giro Cheque will be sent to me very soon.

Al is amazed by ze sights, and films everything wiz 'is new 'super-eighth' Japanese video camera. 'E makes us pose in front of ze newly built aluminium public toilet outside ze Addlestone Sewage Works 'eadquarters, aptly named Sewage House. Torta poses coquettishly on a keep-left bollard in ze middle of Station Boulevard, showing off 'er sawn-off jeans, which barely cover 'er 'ips. Finally, I am forced by Al and Torta's flashing eyes to take zem to our friendly local estate agent, Pees And Queues, an off-shoot of a major national bank which is 'oping to recoup its multibillion Third World losses from commission on British real estate sales. I know they will give Al a 'ard time finding a bargain, though ze idea of Torta being a close neighbour puts me in a moral dilemma.

Ze Pees And Queues agency in Station Boulevard has a wide choice of properties to offer, from tower-block apartments to quaint little semi-attached town houses wiz zer very own little gardens, including one wiz a 'remodernized garden shed,' which excites Al until he sees ze interior of ze house and realizes ze garden shed needs less redecoration zan ze house itself.

We decide to call it a 'jour' and adjourn to ze Dog and Duck where, after ze required number of Gutterspews, Rod promises to come round and see us in the morning. 'E also promises to bring a catalogue wiz photographs of Turkish loos and bidets. I can 'ardly contain myself! Al and Torta treat us to a Pol Pot Pourri take-away and several cans of Spew lager. We cannot complain.

Today is Sunday and we rise early to ze sound of 'eavy snoring from ze guest bedroom. Torta 'as a very passionate snoring voice, which I try to ignore as I help Absinthe prepare ze picnic

47

lunch we are planning for after church. Absinthe is making a typical English picnic: BELT sandwiches (bacon, egg, lettuce and tomato) wiz 'ard-boiled eggs, cold chips and sausages, and a litre of mayonnaise and tomato ketchup; but we cannot resist adding a few bulbs of French garlic to provide a hint of flavour.

I carry a crate of Spew 10X lager out to our new Volvo estate. It is ze pride of my life. I bought it because it is ze ultimate status symbol that no decent Englishman can be without. It is so strong zat it can be driven at high speed into walls and out of ten-storey windows (strange – I 'ave never been to a multi-storey car park wiz windows). Mine is ze very latest model, ze Volvo Estate 'GLXYZ Ejection Ghia': not only does it keep its headlights on day and night, but zer are many other new safety features including a recorded voice as soon as you get into ze car, that shouts 'Fasten your seat belt, Dickhead!' until you 'ave done it. Whatever radio station you tune into, ze programme is regularly interrupted wiz safety commercials telling you not to stop at every pub, to zip up your flies before getting out of ze car if you have a partner wiz you, etc, and zer is automatic braking at red traffic lights and a breathalyser unit built into ze dashboard to tell you not only 'ow many times you are over ze limit, but ze fine and ban you can expect according to which part of ze country you 'appen to be in No wonder ze Swedes are such exciting people! Ze closest France ever came to building an advanced car was ze Citroen ZX wiz its squinting headlights to avoid glare.

I go back into ze cottage and wake up ze Dente's so we will not be late for Free Range communion. Both of zem are completely hungover, except, zat is, for Torta's micro-skirt which barely – I use ze word advisedly – 'angs over 'er waist. I cannot wait to see 'er in 'er cut-away swimming costume when we take 'er to ze Runnynose Municipal Duck and Dive Centre.

Absinthe serves up an excellent English breakfast: prunes, orange juice, All-Bran, bacon and eggs, fried frozen bread, toast and marmalade, and strong Darjeeling Breakfast tea wiz full cream milk – ze most laxative meal known to man. After we 'ave eaten and done ze necessary, we all down a glass of Cornish Pastis to fortify us for Trev ze Rev's sermon in church.

We are greeted at ze church porch by ze verger, E. C. Surplice, who is delighted to welcome Al and Torta as well as our goldfish, Napoleon, which I 'ave brought along in a water-filled plastic bag to join in wiz all ze other animals. We are back to hymns instead of hyrrhs zis week, thank goodness, wiz Trev ze Rev accompanying ze organ on 'is electric guitar, which was given to 'im by a famous pop star from St George's Hills. We sing ze reggae version of 'Sheep May Safely Graze', which sets ze sheep's hoofs tapping, and a 'eavy metal interpretation of 'For Those in Peril on the Sea' which makes my Napoleon wiggle his fins in excitement. It is Trinity Sunday so Trev explains zis difficult concept to us in 'is sermon. Trev is very avant-garde for a rev. 'E is a betting man, and likens ze Holy Trinity to a tiercé, or as you say in England, a tricast, in which you must bet on three horses but, in ze case of ze Trinity, you always win whatever order zey come in. We take ze usual communion of a free-range egg washed down by a glass of Willie Warmer, another of Trev's guest communion ales. On ze way out to ze car Al is flabbergasted: 'That-a service sure knocks-a St Peter's into a cocked-a hat! I can't wait-a to find a place in Addlastona!'

As we drive off, I explain zat we are going a traditional British 'shoulder picnic', so called because we are going to ze famous M25 motorway, which is actually within earshot of Station Approach, where we will sit on ze hard shoulder and eat in comfort, watching ze crazy motorists go by, racing from one jam to ze next or looking in vain for a petrol station. We park on ze hard shoulder just before junction 10 and lay out ze picnic.

'This is fantastico!' Al is ravished, while Torta gives me a ravishing glance of approval as she sucks seductively on 'er banana. After eating, we play ze Addlestone number-plate game. Each side takes it in turns to nominate an oncoming vehicle, zen both sides must make a word out of ze last three letters on ze number-plate, adding as many letters as you want but using ze number-plate letters in order; ze team making ze shortest words wins. Ze first car nominated 'as the plate 'F714 OPK': Al and Absinthe, playing together, cannot make a word, but I make 'p*oppyco*c*k*' which is not very short, but it puts Torta and I in ze lead. Ze next car 'as 'J493 TXD', out of which Torta and I make '*tuxedo*', but Absinthe makes '*taxed*' which is shorter and wins. A car nominated by Al carries 'E208 FKD', which I rule out of order, so 'e 'as to nominate another. In ze end Torta and I win handsomely and she gives me a lingering kiss on ze cheek. It's a good fun game!

We finally run out of lager so zer is no point in staying, and we go back down ze road to Addlestone. Al treats us to a meal at ze

Cloaca Maxima, where we 'ave a typical Italian meal of spaghetti pizza wiz chips and bread and butter, washed down by two litres of ze patron's specially imported Rosso Grottesco which, 'e explains, is matured in ze Roman catacombs.

Back at Five Station Approach we attack ze pastis, because Al complains ze fumes from ze M25 are still affecting 'is delicate throat – 'e will never make an Addlestonian wizout more strength of character. Zer is still a chance 'e will not buy a place in Addlestone! But maybe just Torta could come over and stay wiz us from time to time . . .?

It is ze Dente's last night before zey leave for their grand tour of Britain, so we pop a couple of bottles of Nasti Spewpante zat Al and Torta brought wiz them from Italy. As an ex-sharp-shooter in ze Italian Alpine corps, Al always carries wiz 'im 'is 'borsaglieri' helmet, wiz ze famous floppy black cock feathers, reserved for great ceremonial occasions. 'E suddenly whips ze helmet out from behind 'is chair and leaps to attention, putting it on 'is 'ead wiz a flourish. We all jump to attention in sympathy.

All pulls 'imself up to 'is full height, raises his glass above 'is 'ead to almost six foot from ze ground, lifts 'is eyes to our water-stained ceiling and proposes a toast: 'Signore e Signori, I offer you a toastie to ze glorious historic-a village of Addlastona! Let us get drunk to ze future of this exquisite-a rural retreat, wiz its romantic satellite-dish skyline, quaint-a public offices, beautiful-a red-brick terrace cottages, friendly peasants and, above all, ze famous Giro Choques for "tutto Il mondo"! To La bella Addlastona!'

I think 'e is never going to finish, especially since I am getting thirsty again. We all down our glasses in one and I manage to persuade zem to have an early night because of tomorrow's departure. Once again we are treated to a snoring duet from ze guest room, but no matter, I am in love wiz ze timbre of Tortellina's deep throat.

Next morning, after ze cheap rate time of course, Al asks to make an important business call to 'is secretary in Milan before zey leave. 'E takes over 'alf an 'our. I cannot understand his Italian but 'e 'as sent Torta to zer room to pack and spends most of ze time whispering to 'is secretary about Italian figs, I think. Maybe it is for a new ice-cream flavour 'e plans?

Finally we say our farewells, which take an hour and a half of 'ugging and multiple cheek kissing. Torta gives me a lingering peck on ze lips and a 'eavily eyelashed wink. Zey promise to send us a postcard from ze Lake District, and Torta makes sure I notice 'ow carelessly she climbs into ze Ferrari in 'er mini-micro skirt. As we wave 'au revoir', ze Ferrari roars out of Station Approach Wiz all exhausts and quadraphonic speakers blazing.

Absinthe and I collapse wiz several Cornish Pastis. Tomorrow Rod is coming to give us 'is estimate for repairing ze roof, and bringing a catalogue of Turkish toilets and bidets 'e 'as managed to obtain from France. No need to get up early for ze 'eight-thirty appointment'!

Trev
the
Rev

JUNE

Flaming June in Addlestone. It is ninety degrees – not ze temperature, ze angle of ze rain, which is coming down in escalators!

Amazingly, Rod wakes us up at seven-thirty, not because 'e wants to be early for work but because 'e and 'is team 'ave been at an all-night party in St George's Hills. Rod 'as been 'unting another Rotweiler-country teenage debutante, who 'as promised to 'ave a secret tryst wiz 'im in ze Dog and Duck next week.

Rod and 'is team examine ze roof again and ze water-stained ceilings. After a lot of grim looks and lip-sucking, Rod takes me into ze kitchen for a private consultation.

'I think you might need to sit down and give us both a drink, Monsieur Ash,' Rod puts on ze air of a doctor telling you zat you 'ave cancer. I serve 'im a large can of Spew 10X and a Cornish Pastis for myself.

'The roof, Monsieur Blancmange friend, needs complete re-slating; the joists need replacing in the attic, and the bedroom and ground-floor ceilings need completely re-plastering. Quite a big job, my Froggie friend.' 'E sits back sipping 'is lager wiz a very sad expression on 'is face. I ask 'ow much it will cost. Rod draws a long deep breath.

'Well, Ashy mate, there's all the materials, the labour costs, the overtime, the lunch breaks, the taxi fares, the insurance for my men 'cos it's quite a dangerous job, you must realize, Monsieur Blancmange. Give or take a mile, could be in the region of thirty grand.' 'E purses 'is lips and shuts 'is eyes in apparent agony. I lunge for ze Cornish Pastis bottle.

'But, Rod,' I gasp, 'zat is more zan I paid for ze cottage!'

'If it's that tough, Monsieur Ash, I might be able to flog the cottage for you with enough in your pocket to get back to France, at least second class. I don't know what to suggest, Ash-frog.'

I lunge for my pastis and protest: 'I will never return to

Provence, Rod! I will never leave Addlestone!' I am almost in tears.

Rod smiles compassionately: ''Course, Monsieur Ash, we could try to make it a bit less expensive. As long as you can let us have cash, if you know what I mean? No receipts, of course.'

'Bien sûr, Monsieur Rod. 'Ow much would zat cost?' I ask.

Rod beams at me. 'Probly no more than twelve grand – and I might be able to throw in the bidet and Turkish loo for free.' Perspiringly, I shake 'ands wiz Rod and 'e shows me 'is international catalogue of French bidets and Turkish toilets. Ze bidets are by Minton and Wedgwood, but zere is only one importer of Turkish toilets – our local kebab take-away, who market only one model, ze 'Stand at Ease', used by ze Turkish army. Rod proudly explains zey were originally designed for ze Sultan's guard, ze janissaries. I ask Rod if zat means one foot rest is some way in front of ze other, but 'e shows me ze photograph, which fortunately shows ze foot rests exactly parallel. 'E thinks ze colour could be a problem, because zis year's fashion is Armenian red, but 'e will try 'is best for marron glacé.

Today is ze day of ze shove ha'penny test match at ze Dog and Duck between England and Australia. All England's six players come from Addlestone, which is why we are 'osts to ze contest. But ze Australians are world champions and 'ave just beaten ze West Indies and Pakistan before thrashing former England champions Bolton in a warm-up match. Everybody 'as crowded into ze pub including – 'ow amazing! – a French TV crew; which is making a documentary on Addlestone, Chanel 69 from Paris. We manage to fight our way through to ze barriers, which ze police 'ave erected around ze shove ha'penny board, to where ze England team is waiting in blue denim jeans, red braces, sleeveless tee shirts and luminous slimegreen tattoos. Suddenly, ze cameras start whirring and ze Australian team emerges from ze Gents, resplendent in zer gleaming shove ha'penny couture: Nadir trainers, white leggings wiz cricket pads inscribed 'XXXX OFF', tee shirts wiz thick shoulder pads, white peaked crash helmets wiz ear muffs, luminous sun cream on zer noses and lips, wire mouth shields and padded finger stalls.

I cannot understand why zey 'ave so much equipment for a simple game of shove ha'penny. Wally Connall explains to me zat zey often get mobbed by zer fans and attacked by opposing teams; ze ear muffs are so zat zey will not be put off by abuse from ze opposing crowd.

England loses ze ha'penny toss and Australia puts zem in to shove first. It is a disastrous first shoving. Each player 'as three goes to get ze penny (changed from ze old ha'penny since decimation and inflation) between one of ze parallel lines on ze board. England scores only three out of eighteen goes. Australia attacks ze board wiz antipodean panache: ze police 'ave to pull ze crash barriers back so zat zey can take a long run up to ze board before launching each penny across ze board, which zey do expertly and score sixteen out of eighteen in ze first shoving. England is forced to follow on, but not before we break for tea. Ze Aussies refresh zemselves wiz 'XXXX' while ze English team drowns its sorrows wiz Spew 10X.

After 'tea' England goes in to shove again and makes a remarkable recovery, scoring fifteen wins out of eighteen shoves! But Australia only needs three scoring shoves to win ze test and ze Ashtray. But ze England team is not wizout its loyal sporting Addlestone supporters. Ze England manager, Ian Saccharine, complains about ze light and during ze interval, while Bruiser, ze landlord, takes several minutes to switch on ze lights and ze Aussies take another 'XXXX', carefully laced wiz Bruiser's 'special top', Kev's friends tilt ze board, 'iding chewing gum under one corner and rubbing liquid soap from ze Gents toilet all over ze surface.

Ze Aussies miss every shove except one, so England wins by eighteen shoves to seventeen and regains ze Ashtray. What a glorious victory, England's first since 1934! Ze Dog and Duck erupts in an explosion of Gutterspew effervescence. Ze Ausie team huddles in ze corner by ze Gents, recriminating each other and zer manager, Grant Bruce, for zer ignominious defeat.

A Northern businessman, Mr Ted Giggleswick, who has been watching from ze bar, immediately offers to sponsor Addlestone's England team for ze next test match in ze world series. 'E insists on 'is company slogan being written in large letters on ze Addlestone/England tee shirts. But J. Wally Connall is zer to offer his unbiased advertising advice. 'E asks Ted what is 'is business and what 'e wants to promote. Ted explains zat ze company 'e owns in Yorkshire is a tampon factory which supplies supermarkets wiz zer own-label brands, including Sainsbury's 'Hurdlers' and Safeway's 'Splits', but 'e wants to promote 'is own brand, 'Akimbo'.

Ze smart Addlestone adman is not phased by this challenge. After an investigative chat wiz Mr Giggleswick an several Gutterspews, Wally comes up wiz a brilliant brainwave, slapping 'is forehead. But Wally is a shrewd businessman himself. 'E looks Ted as straight between 'is eyes as 'e is able, given ze number of Spews consumed, and places a forefinger on Ted's yellow-and-red check waistcoat.

'I can solve your dilemma, Ted me old tyke, but I've got to cover my expenses, if you know what I mean.' Wally rubs his thumbs across 'is fingers wiz a cunning smile. 'Readies, naturally.'

Ted understands ze bargaining position immediately, and offers Wally six pints of Gutterspew Extra Strong Export. 'Done!' says Wally wiz a beaming smile and shakes hands furiously wiz Ted. Ted orders ze down payment on 'is contract and Wally launches into 'is advertising campaign presentation.

'As I see it, Ted, your marketing strategy is to flog as many of these Akimbos as you can stuff into the marketplace. Right? You've got the product, which I assume is immaculate in its conception? Ted nods seriously as 'e pulls out a giant cigar and struggles to light it. Wally borrows Rod's blow torch to solve ze problem and carries on wiz 'is presentation.

'Sorry I don't have any flip-flop charts with me, Ted, but we believe in service rather than overheads! By the way it's lunchtime, you couldn't bung me a custard toastie by any chance?' Ted orders ze toastie and three Gutterspew Exports and leans back on ze bar, peering intently through 'is cigar smoke at Wally. Wally carries on.

'We've got the marketing strategy in place, we've done the research, all we need now is the advertising strategy. Now tele-advertising is very expensive, so are all the media, except – as you have wisely sussed, Ted – sports sponsorship, which, if you choose the right up-and-coming sport, can be very cheap, *and* give you lots of exposure, which is what your product needs, if I'm not mistaken?'

Mr Giggleswick is barely visible nodding through 'is cigar smoke. I ask where 'e gets 'is huge cigars, and 'e tells me zey are sold to 'im by a Hungarian count who ran an international Japanese advertising conglomerate called Bashu; ze count was very cold and ruthless so 'e was known as 'minus zero' but 'e always smoked two cigars at a time. Wally continues.

'My in-depth analysis of your requirements, Mr Giggleswick, is that you need to penetrate your market with utmost speed.' Ted can just be seen to nod through the smoke. 'Quite brilliantly, Ted, you have selected the only sport and the only team in the British Isles that has as much as a thousand to one chance of winning a World Cup series, the Addlestone Shovers! May I therefore make so bold as to offer you J. Wally Connall's advertising slogan for your sponsorship campaign?' Ted appears to nod again and orders three more Gutterspews. Wally pulls out 'is Filofax and scribbles notes on blank pages at ze end of ze bar so zat Ted cannot see what 'e is going to present. After ten minutes of intensive scribbling and another Gutterspew, Wally returns to our end of ze bar wiz 'is presentation.

'It may not be Bill Bernbach and 'is electric light orchestra but it's J. Walter Connall's very best creative thinking. 'Scuse me half a sec while I check with my creative director.' Wally uses ze pay phone and speaks in hushed whispers but I manage to 'ear a few words like 'pussy cat' and 'not until Saturday night'. Clearly, Wally receives ze approval of 'is creative department, and rejoins us wiz another pint of Spew to make 'is presentation.

He launches into ze final phase of 'is proposal: 'Based on professional consultation with my creative partner, we have come to the indelible conclusion that there is only one slogan that will work media-wise, cost-effective-wise and impact-wise. Are you sitting comfortably, Mr Giggleswick?' Ted nods through his cigar smoke and Wally pulls out his Filofax sheets. Ze first sheet says 'Copy strategy: to persuade women that they will be more comfortable with Giggleswick "Super, New Improved, High Action, Multi-purpose AKIMBOS"'. Ze second sheet Wally presents says: 'MEDIA SELECTION: Sponsorship of the International Addlestone Shove Ha'penny Champions'.

Wally steps back for another swig of Spew before revealing 'is final Filofax sheet, which 'e reads out wiz pride and pomp: 'The slogan which every player will carry into every test match on the backs of their tee shirts in front of all the TV cameras of the world, bringing peace from nation to nation, will be . . .' Wally pauses for dramatic effect and Ted actually takes ze cigar out of his mouth in anticipation. Wally finally speaks 'The slogan will be: "AKIMBO'S: We'll Help You Shove It!"'

Ze whole pub breaks into applause, except for zose who race for ze Gents. Ze Addlestone Shovers jump all over Mr Giggleswick in anticipation of free tee-shirts, crash helmets and fingerstalls, not to mention a few free Spews! Ze celebration of ze Addlestone Shovers' victory goes on very late. Bruiser, ze landlord, turns all ze lights off and continues serving till three a.m. At three ten we bid Ted and Wally goodnight. As we leave, Rod ze Hod promises again to bring 'is team of experts to start work on ze roof 'tomorrow'. And I thought it was bad in Provence!

Absinthe tells me to 'urry up wiz my farewells because she 'as a strong urge. I am excited and dream of Tortellina lying back in 'er gleaming scarlet Ferrari, but when we get 'ome to Station Approach it turns out 'er urge was just for ze toilet, and she complains again about ze marron glacé bidet and Turkish facilities which Rod promises to install 'tomorrow'.

Next day I 'ave an important lecture at ze Open University car park. Kev and 'is mates are leaving next week for ze south of France, where zey 'ave booked into a super-deluxe campsite which is known for ze Swedish girls who flock zer every summer. I put my deck chair at ze head of ze car park and ze students sit cross-legged on ze tarmac wiz zer Berol pentels poised over zer filofaxes. I start ze lecture wiz essential phrases zey will need in St Tropez:

Nom de plume: We 'ave no plums today.
Poste restante: Rest in Peace, Peter Mayle.
Moules Marinières: Sex on ze beach.
Chateau Briand: Ze French Cheeseburger – meat wiz Brie cheese on.
Force majeur: Ze ability to keep Tory ministers in power when zey 'ave been totally discredited.

Once again ze lecture is interrupted by a rain downpour and we 'ave to race into ze Dog and Duck for shelter. Inside, we meet ze Emeritus Professor of Metaphysics, Des Carts, who insists on lecturing in ze Snug because 'e finds ze vapours in ze car park too strong for 'is metaphysical sensibilities. Des 'as just delivered a lecture on why Kant can't be taken seriously and ze importance of French sexistentialism which preaches ze benefits of feminist love zat is now subsidized by ze Minister of Health, Virgin Lobotomy.

I understand Des's problems wiz ze car park, because every Saturday ze kids who are not allowed into ze pub due to English licensing laws 'ave to stay in zer parents' cars until ze parents are drunk enough to take zem 'ome. Unfortunately, Rod's children get very bored and, while zey are sipping zer lemonade and eating zer Baked Beans and Mayonnaise Ketchup chips, zey stick zer bubblegum on ze other cars' windscreens, which creates a lot of problems when ze owners drive off in ze rain.

Although today's lectures are a wash-out, ze Poetry Society goes ahead in ze evening at ze Coq au Vin. Andronicus 'as promised us all a very stimulating soirée of highly political verses from ze local socialist poet, 'Red Hot' – so called because 'e manages to be very left wing and support fascist Ian Saccharine's football team at ze same time. We all gather in ze back bar of ze wine bar at seven-thirty prompt, wiz our glasses of Entre Deux Merdes at ze ready. Andronicus enters, resplendent in 'is multi-coloured beach shirt and luminous yellow Bermuda shorts, and opens ze proceedings.

'Welcome, man, each and every one, male and female, to this very special evenin' of poetry readin' by our very special guest, Red Hot.' Andronicus gestures to ze bar and a dishevelled creature in sawn-off perforated jeans and a soiled tee shirt bearing ze slogan 'Bognor Regis 1959', lurches towards us, spilling his pint of lager on ze way. He manages to slur a few words of introduction.

'Ladies and gentlemen, dogs, goldfish and mothers-in-law, welcome to this evening of light entertainment. Please understand that the material I shall present has not been past the Tory Party Central Office, although some of it may have been leaked via the Westminster sewage system. I'd like to begin with a few historical verses in honour of the Thatcher Era.

'Maggie, Maggie, Quite Contrary'

Maggie, Maggie, quite contrary,
       How does your fortune grow?
With Sultans and Sheiks and take-over fakes,
       And pretty yes-men all in a row.

Magical Numbers

One two,
       Statistical brew;

Three four,
    The poor are no more!
Five six,
    Jobless tricks;
Seven eight,
    The sick never wait;
Number Ten,
    Run by PR men;
Eleven twelve,
    No right to delve;
Thirteen fourteen,
    No Thames TV reporting;
Fifteen sixteen,
    It's all for privatizing;
Seventeen eighteen,
    Under-inflating;
Nineteen twenty,
    The Treasury's empty!'

Red Hot breaks for ze bar during ze applause, and returns wiz another overflowing pint of amber nectar.

'Thank you kindly, all. I would like to continue with a couple of short pieces of Thatcher forgetabilia. First:

Ride a High Horse

Zeebrugge, Bradford, Clapham, King's Cross,
To see an iron lady upon her high horse;
With cuts on her fingers and cuts on her toes
She shall make bloodshed wherever she goes.

Red Hot pauses for applause and breaks for ze bar once more, zen returns after 'is interval to continue 'is recital. 'Thank you, Ladies, gentlemen, goldfish and mothers-in-law. Sorry, I don't really mean that: I apologize to the goldfish. Finally, an ode to our current government, whose ministers will never resign without being offered a million – quid job in the City, entitled 'The Galumphing Major':

Hey, hey, hip hip hurray
here comes the galumphing Major;
His head held high, his smile awry,

You know he'll keep us out of danger!
When I galloped to power

'Twas Norma's finest hour;
She revelled in our country seat
While I hacked the hot seat in Downing Street.

My Ministers came and my Ministers went,
But I never admitted that any were bent.
There was ne'er a donation my Party could miss:
The Saudis put all in a bank account, Swiss.

Hey, hey, hip hip hurray
I am the galumphing major;
I smile and I squint, 'cos it looks good in print.
I'm just an old Whitehall farce stager.'

Red manages to bow to our applause wizout falling forward, and Andronicus closes ze recital wiz a short rendering from 'is latest Grunge Rap poem, 'Unemployment – I See No Unemployment!'.

'I don't care if I'm black or white;
I can't switch squares 'cos of my colour.
I don't play draughts: half the squares are
banned and duller.
But an Englishman's home is his castle:
So please don't treat me like an ars'le.
If you're goin' to seal my fate:
The black squares count as much as white.
Don't try to check me, mate'

We all redire tired but 'appy after such a cultural evening.
What an exciting evening. Addlestone never ceases to amaze.
What a fantastique choice Absinthe and I made to settle here!

JULY

Z e Queen 'as 'ad her official birthday but, according to Radio Addlestone news, zer is still unrest in ze shires. But, by a brilliant stroke of diplomacy, ze Queen decides to defuse ze problem by privatizing 'erself. She declares zat all of ze Royals will be privatized, and shares in 'Her Maj Enterprises' will be sold on ze Stock Exchange next month. You could never accuse 'er of being a Lésé Majesté.

In a television broadcast, Her Maj announces zat Prince Charles will be sold-off to ze World Wild Life Fund, wiz ze Duke of Edinburgh thrown in free. Lady Di will become a fashion model for Marks and Sparks, opening new stores up and down ze country, but most important, Her Maj will offer 'er services to model Oxfam clothing wiz luminous drape coats, giant wide-brimmed 'ats and 'andbags to match. 'Ow exciting! Zer are several Oxfam stores in Addlestone: perhaps she will come 'ere on 'er tour?

Finally Rod and 'is team arrive to do 'a slightly less temporary' repair to ze roof so zat at least we can sleep wizout ze bucket between us. A pity really, I 'ave grown quite fond of it. After a lot of swearing and several crates of Spew 10X, which I 'ave bought in specially, Rod and 'is lads collapse on our Louis Quinze divan to finish ze last crate of lager.

'Phew!' Rod gasps between slurps. 'It should hold up for a week or two now until we get the slates in, which according to my schedule should be this side of Christmas!' 'E and 'is friends burst out laughing at ze dismay on our faces. 'No, Monsieur Ash, it'll all be finished before the rainy season.'

'But zat is all year round, Rod!' I cry. Rod tries to reassure us zat it will all be over by ze end of ze month – except for ze Turkish loo and bidet which may not be delivered for another six weeks. 'E 'as not been able to get our favourite 'marron glacé' colour, but 'e 'opes it will be 'châtaigne d'eau', which is close.

Absinthe is dejected because she will 'ave to use ze English plumbing for another six weeks, but we console ourselves by listening to Radio Addlestone's Jerry Logan afternoon film review, which is specially produced for ze blind wiz new film clips subtitled in Braille. Zey also announce a new development in Her Maj's Royal privatization plan: ze Royals will 'ire zemselves out for TV game shows and radio programmes! Fergie will appear on *Blind Date*; Prince Charles will appear on *Gardeners' Question Time*; ze Duke of Edinburgh will be in ze *Antiques Road Show* (it is not announced whether as presenter or *object d'art*); Lady Di will be on *Have I Got News For You?*; ze Princess Royal will wave ze flag down ze Aintree course at ze start of next year's Grand National; Prince Andrew will be a contestant in ze *Krapton Factor*. And, wonderfully, ze Queen 'erself will sell tickets for rides in 'er Coronation coach outside Buckingham Palace for five hundred pounds per person, per trip, round Trafalgar House, which 'as always supported ze ex Maggie Thatcher.

Next morning, we read in ze *Addlestone Strumpet* zat our friend, Councillor Kev, is working closely wiz Whitehall and ze MI5 to privatize 'British Air' in order to subsidize ze ever-increasing mountain of Giro Cheque payments so essential to supporting ze expanding British economy. Zey 'ave decided to use Addlestone as a test market to float shares on ze Stock Market. Ze concept is brilliant! Ze air we breathe will no longer be free! From now on, ze British will 'ave to pay tax according to ze lung capacity: ten pounds per cubic inch per month. Zis compulsory tax will be paid into ze coffers of British Air, who will pay dividends to shareholders on a regular basis, except when it is foggy. But ze revenue will go to ze Met Office to 'elp zem forecast violent storms. Before launching ze scheme, Whitehall 'as decided to pilot ze plan over Addlestone, to make sure zer is no political backlash like ze Poll Tax and ze privatization of British Rail's compulsory 'Feet on Seats' policy. So Councillor Kev is very involved in ze publicity for ze share issue, 'andled by ze world-famous Addlestone advertising agency Slouchi and Slouchi who 'ave developed a brilliant slogan: 'Whatever You Pay It's Breathtaking!'

Next afternoon I meet Kev outside ze Runnynose Council offices. 'Can you lend me a quick fiver, my old Blanchmange?' 'e asks. 'I need a taxi to pick up my Giro Cheques.'

'But Kev,' I protest, 'we are just outside ze Council offices. You don't need a taxi, Kev.'

'E winks, and promises never to nudge me again into ze Ladies at ze Dog and Duck. 'Don't worry, Frog mate, I'll claim it back later and give you a half of Gutterspew in recompense.'

I oblige him, but complain zat I 'ave still received no Giro Cheque since I arrived in Addlestone. 'E tells me 'e will pick up an application form when 'e collects 'is Giro Cheques and give it to me when 'e comes zis evening to my final French lecture before 'is holiday in Provence.

At six I arrive at ze Dog and Duck car park wiz my folding chair. Des Cart is already zer wiz his school of Metaphysical students sitting cross-legged on ze tarmac between ze Volvos and ze Ital Marinas.

Finally my students arrive, late as usual: Kev, Rod, Trace and Stace. I give zem zer final lecture before zey race to ze South of France on zer motorbikes. Ze vital phrases are:

Dieu et mon droit: My God, you're right!
Toujours l'amour: Death is forever.
Crêpes flambeés: My shoes are on fire.
L'après-midi d'une faune: Phone me zis afternoon.
Louis Quatorze: Ze loo is on ze fourteenth floor.
Steak tartare: Ze Last Supper.
Hors D'oeuvre: A working woman
Cul de sac: A bunch of arseholes.

Tonight zer is also a new recruit to ze Open University faculty, Jasper Meiggs from Oxford, who 'as resigned as Warden of All Our Souls to take up 'is seat at ze AOU (Addlestone Open University) as Emeritus Professor of Sport and Queueology. 'E is very clever, because 'e got a quadruple first at Balliol in Sporting Classics. 'Is subsequent thesis was in Ancient Chariot Racing and Shove Obol, which is why 'e chose to come to Addlestone and teach our shove ha'penny champions. Jaspers Meiggs is the perfect Oxford don wiz pony tail down to 'is waist, and eighteenth-century breeches.

Jasper's theory is zat ze favourite sport of ze British is queueing, because it is impolite to win, and you must always be behind someone else. Zis goes back to ze traditional British bus queue, which was fanatically observed until ze ethic invasions of ze Fifties. Ze queueing principle is at ze core of British sport: in cricket ze batting team 'as to queue to go in and play; rugby 'as its line-outs and scrums which are 'widened queues'; rowing is so called because ze oarsmen sit in a row and at Oxford ze eights all row in a queue down ze river Isis; even in team games, where all ze players play together simultaneously, ze offside rule applies so zat everyone 'as to come from *behind*, a tug-of-war is actually two opposing queues. As a result, ze British are conditioned always to come second, except, zat is, for ze upper classes, 'o arrange always to be at ze front of ze queue, which is perhaps why zey invented it! What a brilliant academic treatise! Everybody applauds and zen breaks for ze bar in a sprint to show 'ow fit zey are.

Because Jasper is so educated, coming from All Our Souls, ze Brain, Des Cart, Andronicus, Kev and I take 'im across to ze Coq au Vin for a more salubrious bottle of wine or three. 'E 'as only just moved into Addlestone, so 'e still 'as to acclimatize to ze rural life and ze quaint people 'ere. Marie Celeste is wearing 'er usual transparent navel-dipper blouse, zis time wiz a topless bra. We introduce 'er to ex-Warden Meiggs, who chokes on 'is Château Plonqueur '69 when Marie leans forward across ze bar to offer 'im a dumpy pink 'and and a seductive leer.

'I've never met a traffic warden from Oxford before,' she beams. 'You can give me a ticket any time.' A strong gust of air blows across ze bar from 'er flashing eyelashes.

Jasper manages to blurt out: 'Actually I am not a traffic warden, I'm a don.'

Celeste beams again: 'Pleased to meet you, Don.' Ze draught rushes across ze bar again.

Jasper's meticulous academic background doesn't allow 'im to give up: 'It isn't Don, it's Jasper.'

'Oh, Sir Jasper!' Marie cries, leaning back in mock 'orror, pretending to cover 'er cleavage wiz 'er 'and.

Luckily, we are saved by ze sudden entry of Nigel Fortescue-Weather Cock, Bart, accompanied by a new very young lady gleaming in sawn-off psychedelic cycle shorts and a black tank top which reveals more zan just 'er navel.

'Nige Wivacock!' Kev shouts wiz a big smile. 'Another gyno-collegiate weekend in sunny Addlestone, eh?'

Nige looks straight through 'im and presents 'is budding nymphette of at least fifteen summers and, I would say, no winters at all.

'May I present my fianceé, Cher Flashit. We met by chance at the Ottershaw filling station the other day. Cher filled me up and

I felt I just *had* to reciprocate. It's been a whirlwind romance, hasn't it, Cherry baby?'

'Roight,' Cherry Baby replies in immaculate Addlestonian between chews of bubblegum, which she periodically blows out and bursts. It is amazing 'ow democratic ze British aristocracy is: one minute Nige Bart is wiz Lady Cynthia Brille-Laye, ze next wiz a humble petrol attendant.

After two bottles of pink Addlestone Veuve Twankey champagne, most of which is consumed by Cherry Baby, Nige turns to 'er: 'I think we should turn in for an early night, Cherry sweet? You must be very tired after a long day pumping?'

'Roight,' Cherry replies succinctly, and Nige 'elps 'er up ze stairs to ze room 'e 'as permanently booked, bidding us goodnight wiz a weak aristocratic smile.

'Cor, talk about the rich getting the pleasure! "Copulo ergo sum" and a half.' Des Cart philosophizes wistfully.

'I thought she was rather sweet,' Jasper slurs in.

'You'll have to join the queue, traffic warden! Or else pay a hefty parking fine!' Kev can't resist 'is own joke as usual. 'Praps she'd like to 'ave a few private tutorials on sport queueing, one coming behind the other, to use your own terminology?' Kev and Andronicus dissolve into guffaws, wiz ze Brain trying to keep up wiz zem between spluttering coughs wizout losing 'is rolled cigarette.

At ze end of ze evening, we all carry Jasper back to 'is lodgings wiz 'im muttering 'Why did I waste all those years at Oxford when I could have met intellectuals like Marie and Cher when I was young?' All further mutterings are incomprehensible, or 'sotted voce' as Kev calls it. We break up and retire our separate ways to gain strength for another day. In bed, I cannot decide whether to dream of Tortellina, Marie Celeste or Cherry Baby. I wish we still 'ad ze bucket in ze bed. Maybe zer will be another 'urricane soon.

Today it is Saturday, and ze Addlestone Friday football ground 'osts ze annual tug-of-war combined wiz a beauty contest to choose ze Princess for ze Black Gooseberry Fair due to be 'eld in a week's time. Ze event is billed as ze 'Lout and Pout Contest, sponsored by ze Red Herring Fish 'n' Chip Shop in ze High Street'. 'Lout' refers to ze heroic tug of war contestants, male and female, and 'Pout' refers to ze Black Gooseberry Princess contestants. So as not to be sexist or ageist, ze Princess Contest is open to all ages and sexes. Ze judging takes place in ze Nissen hut bar. Each contestant is introduced by Councillor Kev, who has taken on ze role of compère.

Ze contestants are resplendent in zer Sunday dresses – all, zat is, except ze one male entry, Gaffer George who worked at ze nearby film studios in ze 1950s, and is wearing white slacks and a sleeveless shirt to show off 'is tattoos. Kev asks each one what zer interests are, and what is ze most important thing zey would change in ze world if zey had ze power. Ze young girls all say zey would protect ze environment and ze ozone layer, but Granny Sleet, wearing a polka-dot mini-skirt and crisp white-rinse hair, emphatically plumps for 10p off ze price of a pint of Gutterspew Mild, which swings ze judging panel, she wins by a white whisker and is chosen Princess of the Black Gooseberry Fair to ze rapturous applause of ze audience. Gaffer George comes second, wiz Andronicus's stunning seventeen-year-old daughter, Kimberly, third. George and Kimberly will be maids-in-waiting to Granny Sleet.

Outside on ze football pitch, ze tug-of-war is reaching its climax, wiz Addlestone Social Club in ze final against ze Thrope Park Terriers. It is a mixed contest, wiz ze women even more rotund and solid zan ze men. Front man for Addlestone is Bruiser Reade from ze Dog & Duck wiz as anchorman, Andy Lyons from ze Taxi Tavern' (so-called because it is next to ze CAB tower block, ze Citizens' Advice Bureau).

Apparently zer is no love lost between Andy and Bruiser, especially since zey run rival watering 'oles. Ze Addlestone team is carrying a lot of impressive ballast, including Kev's mother-in-law, but Thrope Park 'as ze largest ladies in ze area, who will take some pulling. Ze whistle is blown and both sides take ze strain. Addlestone gains a few inches, but zen ze Thrope ladies start to gain ground. One lady is even 'olding ze rope between 'er teeth so zat she can use 'er hands on ze ground. Slowly Addlestone loses ground: zey are close to being pulled across ze centre line.

Suddenly, Andy shouts from ze back: 'Come on, Bruiser, PULL! Imagine you're pulling the milkman off your missus!' At which point Bruiser drops ze rope and races back in fury to get Andy, who has already dropped ze rope and is racing for ze hedge. Ze rest of ze Addlestone team collapse on ze grass in 'eaps of giggles (including Kev's mother-in-law, who is almost unrecognizable wiz a smile on 'er face), while Andy dives through ze fence, 'otly pursued by Bruiser. Thrope wins by an easy pull-over and is awarded ze yellow jersey.

Ze chairman of ze Red Herring Fish 'n' Chip Shop presents ze Thrope team wiz battered plaice and chips take-aways in presentation cartons. Ze Addlestone team retires to ze Dog and Duck to drown zer sorrows, which zey manage to do wizout much sorrow. Bruiser reappears saying 'e never caught Andy, 'o seems to 'ave gone into 'iding.

Next morning we go to ze Free Range Church for ze common-denominational service. It is another women's Sunday so, unfairly I think, ze cows and farm animals are excluded. Ze preacher is Lesley Bian once again, who is wiz us because it is 'Single Parenting Sunday'. Lesley explains to us zat ze great Lordess in 'er wisdom ordained zat men were only created from Eve's body in order to provide procreation until such time as medical science developed sperm banks so zat men could provide ze necessary wizout getting any real pleasure. Councillor Kev and 'is wife Mave, together wiz Jasper Meiggs and a friend, are sitting next to us keeping up appearances for ze feminist vote, so I ask Kev in a whisper what is a sperm bank. 'E replies it must be Barclays and guffaws as silently as 'e can into 'is Ancient and Modern hyrrh book. After ze service we I all break for ze Dog and Dog and much needed 'Spew-fuls'.

Jasper 'as a young friend wiz him from Oxford, Johnnie, a junior fellow from Balliol who Jasper met originally on 'oliday in Mykonos. Zey are obviously very good friends. Johnnie is a Latin professor, and Jasper wants 'is 'elp wiz 'is classical Sport and Queueology course, because 'e thinks it is important for ze shove ha'penny team and ze other students to appreciate ze crudiments of ze Latin language in order to understand ze origins of modern shove ha'penny and British queueing. Johnnie will be delivering a Latin lecture at ze AOU tomorrow.

After a long lunchtime session, Absinthe and I retire to Five Station Approach wiz our Sunday take-away treat – jamburgers, fried butties and chips wiz mayonnaise. We tune in to Jerry Logan's late show and ze ten o'clock news. Ze English 'ave very strange pronunciation of foreign places, using upper class long 'A' whenever they can: 'Irahq', 'Irahn', 'Ahfghahnistahn',

'Croahtia', 'Ahlbahnia', 'Bahsque' separatists, et ceterah. Kev says you can always tell when zer's going to be another war because ze newscasters all go to ze Angela Ripoff school of electrocution to learn to repronounce ze names so we don't recognize zem any more. When zey start saying 'Ahddlestone', zat's when we should emigrate on ze next plane.

Next morning, Monday, Absinthe and I go 'unting for bric-à-brac down ze High Street. We spend ages in ze famous flea shop, Trish Trash, which 'as an amazing collection of secondhand items at smack-down prices. We are enthralled by ze range of antique junk: tea sets, old fire grates, fire irons, egg-timers, decorated mirrors, prehistoric 'oovers and sewing machines, baby bootees, a weight-lifting bar, a glass jar full of used golf balls and a packet of a 'undred white plastic forks, opened but apparently not used. What treasures! So much more exciting zan our street markets in Provence.

In ze evening I am not teaching at ze Open University, but I go along to ze car park to 'ear Johnnie's inaugural lecture. 'E introduces ze students to some useful Latin phrases:

Fiat lux: An expensive Italian car;
Benedictus Benedicat: Thank God you didn't forget the
    Benedictine!
Ars gratia artis: For the sake of the bottom line;
Carpe diem: The wife's daily moan;
Caveat emptor: Beware of the dustbin man;
Summa cum laude: I spent my Summer hols with Nikki Lauda;
Gloria in excelsis deo: Glory to Chelsea's Peter Osgood.

Ze students respond well, but Johnnie 'as difficulty in getting zem to understand zat ze philosophical expressions *a priori* and *a posteriori* are not sexual positions.

When we get back to Five Station Approach we turn on Radio Addlestone and catch ze late night news. Apparently, zer 'as been industrial unrest at ze Sewage Works, wiz a sit-in, and Eddy Culvert's son 'as been arrested for blowing 'is own crumpet. I am a little bit angry wiz Absinthe's eye-flashing at Jasper's young friend, Johnnie, so I sleep in ze guest room wiz my favourite bucket filled wiz a hot-water bottle.

Life is so full in rural Addlestone. I cannot imagine 'ow our French friends zink we 'ave nothing to do. I cannot wait for next Saturday and ze Black Gooseberry Fair, especially to see

Andronicus' lovely young daughter as maid-in-waiting. I go to sleep tired but 'appy wiz my warm bucket.

Next morning ze postman delivers a miracle! It is not actually my Giro Cheque, but ze application form which Kev 'as kindly arranged for me. I am very excited and fill in ze form straight away.

Councillor Kev is not much in evidence zese days, because 'e is busy on ze Addlestone 'Docklands' project. 'E is trying to raise money from Brussels to fund a Portakabin office complex down by ze canal. 'E calls it 'Budgie Wharf'. Also, 'e is working 'ard on ze first Addlestone Film Festival, due to be held next month. Zer will be a wide selection of unpublished footage from great movies as well as regular films and new releases. Ze films will be previewed on Radio Addlestone. So far no international stars 'ave agreed to attend, but we 'ave written to Jeremy Beadle to ask 'im to open ze Festival.

Finally, ze day of ze Black Gooseberry Fair arrives! Ze 'ole town is dripping wiz bunting designed as Giro Cheques, and loud-speakers playing Ugandan rap music from every lamp-post, wiz a commentary from Jerry Logan. Ze 'ole town is alive wiz visitors from as far away as Ottershaw and Chertsey. At 10.30 ze streets are lined wiz expectant faces as ze parade begins.

Ze route is from ze station, down Citizens Advice Avenue, along Giro Drive and into ze High Street before turning off to Addlestone Friday's football ground. Ze parade is headed by ze town traffic warden, 'o rather slows zings up by stopping to give out parking tickets on ze way. 'E is roundly jeered and booed by ze crowd. Following in 'is wake is ze Lollipop Lady Brigade, six-strong, marching in formation and resplendent in zer uniforms, twirling zer lollipop sticks above zer 'eads and lifting zer knees as 'igh as arthritis will allow, a perfect team of majorettes. Next comes ze First Addlestone Brownie Pack band, led by Trev ze Rev wearing 'is green golfing dog-collar and singing 'Onward Christian Brownies' on 'is guitar.

Zen comes ze Princess 'erself, Granny Sleet leaning on 'er Zimmerframe on ze back of a Toyota pick-up truck, wearing a scarlet wedding gown rented from ze local fancy-dress shop. Everybody cheers wildly. Be'ind ze Princess come ze 'maids in waiting', ze beautiful Kimberly and Gaffer George, both in long bridesmaid dresses, standing up through ze sun roof of Nige Bart's Marina Lagonda Turbo, driven by ze local estate agent Stu Potter.

Next come ze floats led by Age Concern, wiz a jazz band consisting of even more geriatric players zan ze Zimmerframe Dooh-Daah Band; zen comes ze Runnynose Council's Housing Benefit float, consisting of a brilliant replica of Addlestone's Cardboard City, wiz genuine tramps supplied by ze Waterloo Casting Agency and psychedelic grafitti courtesy of Winston Thatcher's students. Ze float 'as a banner: GIRO RULES OK! Ze rear of ze parade is brought up by ze Addlestone Chamber of Commerce riding zer mountain bikes in formation, and led, rather unsteadily, by ze Brain, coughing between two rolled cigarettes in 'is mouth, wiz two behind each ear – today 'e's taking no chances; each rider is wearing a tee shirt wiz ze slogan 'Never Knowingly Oversold'.

Absinthe and I follow ze parade to ze football ground, where zer are many different stalls and exciting games to play. Ze Amalgamated Churches of Addlestone 'ave a stand wiz grafitti on ze sides saying 'Hell Ain't Cool' and 'Christians Solar-Powered by the Son' – zey 'ave a 'What the Butler Saw' machine for 20p a go, 'Strictly over 18s only – ID to be shown'. Ze local funeral director, Bernie Pire, is running a tombola, wiz a free cremation as ze main prize and free embalming for ze runners-up. You can buy every type of local produce, from dried dandelions wiz dried dock leaves, Gucci shoelaces from ze Oxfam stall and reconditioned condoms wiz home-made jam flavour, to runny icecream and rice-pudburgers.

Absinthe 'as a go at 'Hunt the Whole Egg' in a tray of saw-dust, but in three goes only finds empty, broken shells. I try my luck at 'Hook the Knicker', a stall where zer is a strong jet of air blowing numbered knickers into ze air which you 'ave to catch as zey fly about, using ze 'ook on a fishing rod. I score two knickers and five points, which entitles me to a squashy spider or three more tries. I want to try again because it is fun, but Absinthe drags me away, so I donate ze squashy spider to 'er. Ze most exciting attraction is 'Indiana's Trail', a sort of 'aunted 'ouse, but where ze children 'ave to negotiate fiercely wobbling walkways at different levels. Suddenly, on ze top floor, out of one of ze doorways, ze Brain appears, staggering even on ze non-wobbly sections. 'Where's ze Gents?' 'e shouts wiz urgency. 'E lurches along ze wobbly parapet, wiz one 'and on ze guide rail and ze other holding 'imself, losing 'is balance on several occasions punctuated by loud swearing. Ze spectators, especially ze children, are enraptured, cheering and applauding every stumble and swear-word. Eventually, 'e slides down ze wobbly staircase to ze exit and sways round ze back, out of sight but not out of earshot, and wizout losing zis rolled cigarette!

On ze way out, ze Dog and Duck 'as a small stand piled 'igh wiz white tiles: 'Buy a Tile for Our Gents'. Sharon, ze landlord's beautiful daughter, persuades us to buy one. She says it is to cover up and eliminate ze grafitti. I feel a little sad because I 'ave learned a lot of English from zose walls. As we pass ze Free Range Church zere is a sign outside, 'Medieval Food in Church Hall', but we already 'ave our rice-pudburgers, which we plan to 'eat up in ze microwave when we get back to Station Approach.

Rod the Hod

AUGUST

Normally ze front page of ze *Addlestone Strumpet* is packed wiz arson, rape and pillage, but today ze headline story is very exciting: Addlestone Joins the ERM With Its own Coinage!

Addlestone 'as gone where ze British government was too scared to stay: ze European Exchange Rate Mechanism. What guts Councillor Kev 'as! I read zat Addlestone will issue its very own coinage called 'stones'. Zey will be used as tokens so zat people will be able to barter and exchange goods wizout using real money at all! Soon, ze 'stone' will be quoted on ze Stock Exchange and ze Hung Sin Index in Hong Kong. In fact, it is already quoted at two pfennigs against ze Deutschmark. Stones can also be deposited at ze Addlestone Portakabin Building Society in ze High Street.

THE QUARTER POUNDER

In order to facilitate circulation, 'ere will be stone dispensing machines in every pub. I zink Kev would make an excellent Chancelor of ze Exchequer!

Finally, ze Addlestone Film Festival opens in ze Co-op car park, where one wall 'as been whitewashed to provide a giant screen. Ze proceedings are introduced by ze Brain, who explains ze week's programme through a microphone and 'is rolled cigarette. To cut costs, every film 'as a sponsor. Ze Festival will open with ze first screening of *Gone with the Wind* in 4-D Smellivision, sponsored by Andrex. Zen zer will be a remake of *Ben Hur*, re-titled as *Ben Him* by ze Runnynose Council censorship department, which is very anti-sexist. Because Jeremy Beadle declines to be about in Addlestone, ze committee 'as asked ze star of *Ben Him*, Ollie Reade, to open ze première riding through ze High Street to ze car park in an ancient chariot wearing Roman dress, but ze police refuse permission on ze grounds of drunken chariot driving. So ze Brain announces between coughs zat ze première will be opened by an old pensioner, Granny Berry, because she used to drive a cart and horse delivering rotting gooseberries – hence ze origin of Black Gooseberry Fair. *Ben Him* is sponsored by ze local second-hand car dealer; Bangers 'n' Smash.

Ze next film on ze programme is a presentation of *Brief Encounter*, sponsored by Y-Fronts. Finally, ze Festival terminates wiz a remake of ze *Big Sleep*, sponsored by Carlton TV and starring Humphrey Bogart look-alike Dustbin Offman and Lauren Bacall lookalike Merle Stripp, who manages to keep her clothes on for ze whole film!

Ze fame of ze Festival 'as spread all over ze world, and we are honoured by ze visit of ze internationally famous Italian producer and director, Frederico Fellatini, who arrives in 'is private 'elicopter from Rome, together wiz 'is renowned harmonica player, Ennio d'Iron, who once wrote for Lonnie Donegan before composing ze famous themes for Fellatini's 'Fusilli Westerns'. In honour of ze magnificent visit, ze Runnynose Council lays out ze red lino on ze roof of ze Citizen's Advice Bureau tower block. Ze Lord Mayor, Cliff Roakes, leads ze Arts Committee to welcome ze distinguished guests as zey alight from ze helicopter.

Fellatini is immaculate in a dazzling white linen suit and white panama,' d'Iron wears a black tee shirt, black jeans and beard to match. But wiz zem zer is also a very beautiful, very young, blonde lady 'holding on to 'er straw hat and wearing a flowing diaphanous peach-coloured dress, which swirls in ze air turbulence and causes its own as it becomes clear she is wearing no bra.

As zey step down and trip over ze fraying red lino, Mayor Roakes moves forward to introduce us, wearing 'is official regalia, ze lime-green blazer and pink flannel flares wiz ze pewter Gutterspew-mat mayoral chain 'anging down to 'is enormous waist. We all say 'hi!' and Fellatini introduces ze young lady as 'is daughter, Peccata Cardinale, a budding Italian actress wiz a great future. Ze *Addlestone Strumpet* photographer is zer wiz 'is Brownie to record ze occasion for posteriority. Unfortunately, ze turbulence from ze helicopter blades blows Cliff's toupee over ze parapet and down below, where, we discover later, it lands in ze 'Keep Addlestone Tidy' bin. So ze photo-call is cancelled, and we all adjourn to ze Cloaca Maxima for Negroni's and an Italian buffet: Avocado congrappa, Spaghetti alla Cloaca, Steak Carbonizzata, Chocolate Ice with Fernet Branca.

Over dinner, Ennio serenades us wiz 'is harmonica, playing 'Arrivederci, Roma', 'O Sole Mio' (which excites ze local cobbler, Jim Last, 'o 'appens to be 'aving a champagne supper in ze corner of ze restaurant wiz a young lady old enough to be 'is daughter) and 'Nessun Dorma' ze Italian alarm clock aria. During ze digestifs – Fernet Branca for ze Italians and Spew 10X for ze rest of us, at Brian Damage's insistence – ze great director, Fellatini, explains zat 'e 'as brought one of 'is videos for us to show during ze Festival: *4½* – unfortunately severely edited down from ze original *8½* version, due to Runnynose Council censoring out ze fully clothed scenes. Mayor Cliff fumbles wiz ze gold chain of office inside 'is shirt, and apologizes effusively, offering another drink in compensation. 'E promises to find a sponsor for ze screening, maybe ze local turf accountant, Bill Tor, provided ze film can be re-titled *9 to 2*. Signor Fellatini graciously agrees and munificently offers us another round of digestifs. Kev asks Ennio d'Iron for a harmonica request.

'Signor Any Old Iron, would you grace me wiv the pleasure of playing the famous aria from the first act of what I call the "Hippy Birds Eye Opera" by Jack Puccini, "Your Tiny Finger's Frozen"?' Kev breaks into 'is guffaw routine, but luckily I am out of nudging range. Ennio bows proudly, adjusting his moustache. 'It is-a my pleasure, signore.'

As Ennio begins 'is recital, Frederico lights another Davidoff cigar and gives us a toast: 'I wish your Festival success.' We all drink to each other. 'Now I will tell you why I *really* came to Addlestone.' We are all agogo. Signor Fellatini waves to Signor Ennio to stop playing and sit down at ze table while 'e makes 'is speech.

'*Naturalmente* I am here to enjoy your festival of international movie masterpieces – including mine of course. But I have an ulterior motive. Ever since I tuned in to Radio Addlestone in Rome, I have realized that Addlestone is a unique society, comparable to Eboli and the beautiful unspoilt villages of Southern Italy. So I am here because I have a new idea for a film about peasant folk and the injustices which they have to endure from their masters, especially state bureaucracy, which is particularly strong in this country of course. If you agree, Mayor Roakes, Film Chairman Damage, I would like to propose shooting a film about the cruelty of bureaucratic oppression – based in Addlestone!'

Frederico leans back for a long puff on 'is cigar, while ze

Mayor and Arts Committee draw breath in amazement.

'What exactly do you have in mind, Signor Fredico?' ze Brain splutters out between coughs and wheezes at ze same time as taking a quick slurp on 'is Gutterspew through 'is cigarette.

Signor Frederico leans forward and points 'is cigar at ze Brain: 'To quote your friend Rodge, the concept for the film is "cosmic". Let me outline the plot.' Signor Frederico orders another Fernet and begins 'is presentation.

'The title of the film is *Once Upon a Time in Addlestone*. It is a Spaghetti Take-Away Western. It is about a small rural village in Surrey, where the villagers and traders are being terrorized by a gang of bandits called the Vatman Boys, from London. The bandits threaten to take everything the villagers own, until one day, into the village rides an unknown stranger on a Yamaha 3500cc motorcycle. He is very quietly spoken, and chews garlic bubblegum while smoking reconstituted Woodbines, but he has a heart of gold and empty wallet to match. He makes friends with the local Mother Superior and is put up at the local convent. The Mother Superior keeps our hero up all night explaining the predicament of the village and the terror threatened by the Vatman Boys. Our hero, who the villagers now call "Anon", agrees to defend them against the evil marauders, who have said they will come at noon for their dues. Anon takes up his position in a rocking chair on the pavement outside the Tandoori Take-Away to await their arrival. This is where Ennio does his bit, playing the main theme from *The Man with Bubblegum in his Harmonica*, while Anon rocks slowly in his chair, chewing pensively and smoking his Woodbine, brushing away the wheely-bin flies from his own. As the sun climbs lazily to high noon, the Mother Superior deserts him, of course, guilty about her night of sin.

'At the stroke of noon on the dot, the Vatman Boys come cruising down the High Street in their gleaming scarlet XJ 220 Jaguar, but they stop on the level crossing, because Anon has cleverly erected a cardboard lollipop lady to halt them. Out of the Jaguar step the four Vatman Boys in low-brimmed hats and ankle-length, black loden coats; grim-faced, with dark glasses and brandishing warrants flashing in the sunlight. Anon screws up his eyes and nods towards the level crossing gate-house. This is the signal! The level crossing gates come crashing down and trap the Vatman Boys on the railway line. Suddenly, at great speed, the 12.02 from Egham comes hurtling down the line, amazingly on time, smashing through the Jaguar and dragging the Vatman Boys beneath it, screaming all the way to Weybridge.

'Anon gets up slowly from the rocking chair, tosses his Woodbine into the wheely-bin and rides off into the sunset, without so much as a backward glance at the Mother Superior, who has come out of the shadows with the other townsfolk to wave the nameless hero a tearful farewell.'

Ze 'ole restaurant erupts into loud applause and cheers at ze conclusion of such a brilliant exposition. Frederico bows and orders drinks for everyone. We all drink a toast to ze shooting of *Once Upon a Time in Addlestone*. Fellatini insists it will be shot on location 'ere in a few months' time: 'I reject *completamente* the cardboard sets of Shepperton or the back streets of Liverpool tarted up with phoney road signs to look like Addlestone. I want *cinéma vérité* – the real thing!'

The eyes of Angelo Gabbi, ze Cloaca's owner, nearly explode wiz delight as 'e starts to plan 'undreds of meals for ze Itie crew. 'E immediately offers our table another round of grappas and Fernet Brancas. By now, Kev and ze Brain are slumped against ze wall, wiz zer heads together: ze Brain is snoring wiz 'is still-lit cigarette hanging from 'is lower lip. After five minutes of shaking, we manage to wake zem up. Federico thanks us profusely for our hospitality, and 'e leaves wiz Ennio and Peccata for zer rooms at ze Coq au Vin. Wally Conall, Titus Andronicus, Cliff Roakes and I 'elp ze Brain and Kev to zer doorsteps, and leave zem to ze mercy of zer respective wives. Unfortunately, we discover next day zat in our euphoria we delivered zem to ze wrong wives. But zer is no problem: probably ze wives enjoyed shouting at a different husband for a change. All in all it 'as been a very successful film festival for our tiny village.

Early next morning, Kev and Rodge ze Dodge are off to St Tropez. Absinthe and I turn up at ze bus station to wish zem well. Kev is groaning from ze night before, and muttering about a coach company zat is so badly organized its coaches leave before ze pubs open.

'I'll never remember all those Frenchie phrases, Ash mate,' Rodge shakes 'is 'ead ruefully. 'Except, of course "Volley-voo cooshay ave moy, sir sewer".'

I try to reassure 'im, and say zat, in a country like France, gestures speak louder zan words.

'Cosmic, Ash!' Rodge gives me an 'ard stare. 'How on earth do you gesture when you want something like *that*?'

I am obviously not being very 'elpful. I tell 'im just to do 'is best, and 'e assures me wiz a wink zat 'e certainly will. Kev grunts.

I notice zat, in addition to zer rucksacks, zey 'ave a large black bag. 'What's zat?' I ask.

'It's our doctor's bag,' Rodge explains.

'Very sensible, Rodge. Maybe you could give Kev somezing now to make 'im feel better?' I suggest.

'Naah, me old tadpole,' Rodge shakes 'is 'ead. 'There's no medicinal whisky in it.' 'E leans close and winks: 'Just a few titivators for the ladies, understand? Even Kev's gotta have a bit of a rest occasionally.' 'E gives me a nudging cackle and 'elps Kev on to ze coach. We wave as zey drive off, Rodge beaming evilly, Kev slumped against ze window. Berkeley Tours disappears over ze level crossing on ze road to paradise.

When we get back to Station Approach, Rod 'ze Roof', as we 'ave renamed 'im, is waiting outside in 'is long-past-use-by-date pick-up truck, asleep at ze wheel wiz Radio Addlestone's *Gold Top Pop* show, sponsored by A.I.D.S., blaring out of ze window. Strangely, zer are two large boxes on ze back of ze truck.

'I didn't know you were coming, Rod,' I say, waking 'im up.

'Nor did I, Mister Mange-Tout,' 'e sighs. 'The gear only arrived at my yard this morning. Thought you'd want it right away.'

Ze gear turns out to be our Turkish toilet and bidet. Unbelievable, Rod explains ze lads are round ze corner grabbing something to eat at ze 'Sani Shop', and will be back in a minute. An hour later, ze lads return from ze 'shop' wiz a crate of Super Spew 10X and offload ze boxes. Ze bidet pack is opened first and, horror upon horror, ze colour is not 'marron glacé', nor even 'châtaigne d'eau' but 'chocolate mousse'. Absinthe and I look at it in dismay.

Eventually, we 'ave to tell Rod we can't accept it; ze colour just doesn't go wiz our diet – we never eat chocolate. Reluctantly, Rod agrees to send it back, and zey reload it on to ze truck, but not before finishing ze crate of lager.

Rod explains zat ze roof tiles will be a little while yet, so I ask why 'e can get delivery of a toilet suite from France before simple roof tiles from England. I obviously do not understand ze intricacies of British manufacture and distribution. Rod explains it to me and points out zat our tiles were specially made for ze cottages in Station Approach, 'ave been out of production for many years, and need to be redesigned and re-manufactured.

'Not to worry, Mister Blanche-Tout,' Rod assures us, 'we should have them by the end of the month. I'm sorry about the chocolate mousse, I'll get the "shatin do" as quick as I can.' And off ze lads go once again.

Tonight is Bingo Night at our Bingo Hall just round ze corner. We 'ave never been before, so Wally Connall and his large wife, Shirl, 'ave kindly agreed to take Absinthe and me and show us ze strings. Zey collect us at six. Wally is in 'is smart adman's summer casualwear: a denim-blue shell suit and open-toed trainers; Shirl is in a white cotton see-through blouse and pink leggings, which she wears remarkably well considering she is not an ounce over fifteen stone. On ze way to ze hall, via ze Coq au Vin, Wally explains zat tonight, for ze first time, zer will be a new bingo game called 'Flingo', created by Addlestone's famous inventor, Alan Stein. It is based on horse races, which are projected on to ze screen. For each race you 'ave a bingo card wiz numbers on it, and if you get a line up out of ze first six horses you shout 'Flingo!' and win a prize. Kev's wife, Mave – 'o 'as not gone to St Tropez wiz him – wins one race and receives a magnificent plastic sherry decanter. Shirl wins another race and an ingenious new device just invented by Al Stein, a chipboard-faced toilet-roll dispenser, like a cigarette machine, holding up to twenty-five rolls. It is designed for domestic use, but Wally tells me 'e is preparing a sales campaign to distribute zem to Indian restaurants.

As we stroll back down ze High Street, I notice zer is a new cycle shop, 'Cyclops', which I remark on to Wally. 'E laughs.

'No, Ash! It's the new opticians. He charges one eye at a time. Clever name though, isn't it? I thought it up. And I'm doing the advertising for them as well. I've got a great slogan: "Eye'll see you right – at Cyclops!" Not bad, eh? They do free eye-testing while you wait. And they're selling revolutionary new contact lenses that change colour and go dark at night to help you to sleep – they were invented by Al Stein as well.'

Wally kindly agrees to introduce me to Mr Stein, who I am very interested to meet. Further down ze High Street, I am amazed to see an ad in ze window of ze personnel agency, 'chores' (slogan: chores – choose yours), which reads 'Various Interesting Positions Offered – from £6,000 p.a.'. I didn't know zey had moved into ze girlie business. How exciting; it is so much more sophisticated zan ze cards in ze telephone kiosk – although ze last one I saw intrigued me, 'Scratch 'n' Sniff: phone Lil 64393'. But £6,000 is very expensive, even for Nige Bart. 'P.a.' surely cannot mean per act? The price must cover a special subscription, perhaps open-ended? I want to ask Wally about it, but I am afraid to in front of Absinthe in case she gets suspicious. But I plan to find out later.

We stop for ze inevitable multiple nightcap in ze Dog and Duck. In ze far corner I notice someone leaning against ze wall zat I 'ave not seen before. 'E is a big man, but not more zan six-foot six tall, and no wider zan a Gutterspew truck. As we say in Provence, 'e is built like a terracotta outhouse. 'E 'as a glazed look in 'is eye as 'e chews 'is gum wiz a yellow cigarette between 'is lips, and flips a coin at regular intervals. 'E is in a sleeveless green-and-brown flak jacket, which reveals a barrel-size belly hanging over 'is blue jeans. 'Is pointed egg-shaped skinhead needs a shave. It will always need a shave. 'Is arms are thicker zan Bayonne hams and 'is fist makes 'is pint look like a liqueur glass. Ze tattoos on 'is arms 'ide ze colour of 'is skin, which is festooned wiz what looks like distressed maidens surrounded by Kalashnikovs and Magnums, not ze champagne variety. Through ze forest on 'is chest I can just make out what seems to be a passable full-length portrait of Humphrey Bogart next to a stitchless Lauren Bacall. Wally shouts to 'im to come and join us. 'E peels 'imself from ze wall and waddles towards us, 'is earrings jangling like triangles in ze London Philharmonic Orchestra.

'Ash, Absinthe, meet Rick, our resident private detective. Addlestone's Philip Marlowe.'

Rick takes my hand and squeezes out all sensation. Thank goodness I am left-handed.

'Glad to meet you, Mister Mange-Tout,' 'e says slowly, grinning between clenched teeth. 'I knew a Frenchman once in Morocco – when I was working in the Blue Budgerigar night club one holiday in the heart of the Casbah. His name was Claude Pluies. Mean anything to you?' I shake my head. 'He was a great guy. Used to steal the beach lilos from under the Germans' noses. Knew all the joints in town. There was nothing we couldn't fix between us. Whenever a girl got into trouble she'd come to Rick. They'd always get what they wanted. At a price of course.'

'E takes a long drag on 'is Black Sobranie and looks wistfully into ze distance, which happens to be in ze direction of ze Ladies. But 'e actually excuses himself and goes to ze Gents. 'E is very courteous. I think 'e cannot be an Addlestonian. As 'e turns and walks away I see 'e 'as a tiny pony tail sprouting out of ze back of 'is naked scalp. Maybe 'e is Addlestonian after all.

'He's known as Rick the Dick,' Wally tells us. 'He's solved some pretty big cases in his career. Ask him.'

Rick saunters back to ze bar and I ask 'im about 'is thrilling and dangerous business. 'E takes a long puff on 'is yellow Black Sobranie and blows ze smoke up to ze faded brown ceiling.

'Yep. It's not a game for school-leavers. Although I did get a top GCSE grade in birdwatching. You need your wits about you and a bottle of scotch in your hip pocket, so you can defend yourself without being accused of having an offensive weapon. I don't take any sort of dirty business. Just credit control, repo,' – Wally whispers to me that means repossessions – 'and the right sort of freelance bailiff work. And divorce work, naturally. Who's sleeping with who, where, when and how often. I'm consultant on the Royals to one of the biggest tabloids in the solar system. They pride themselves on investigative journalism. They're the journalists, I'm the investigator. It's been pretty busy recently as you might have noticed.'

'Do you think you are morally justified to undermine Britain's glorious monarchy, Rick?' I venture nervously while swiftly offering another round of drinks.

Rick takes another long puff and blows another cloud of pungent smoke to ze ceiling. 'E gives me a long hard stare, grinning through 'is clenched teeth and cigarette.

'Sure thing, buddy,' 'e drawls. 'My motto is, to quote the master: Down these mean gutters man must go who is not himself a guttersnipe. I just serve. I leave moralizing to the rich and the politicians – if there's any difference. 'E takes a dramatic gulp from ze triple scotch 'e asked me to order for 'im. What amazing characters zer are in Addlestone!

It is now ze school 'olidays, and ze lovely streets of Addlestone are not clogged every morning and afternoon wiz mothers cycling to and from school wiz children strapped to carry seats wearing 'elmets smothered wiz Triassic Park stickers. Addlestone is more peaceful and charming zan ever.

Even ze vandals 'ave gone on 'oliday to Germany, where zey

say ze shop-window plate glass offers more of a challenge, and ze bar furniture is much more solid. Ze Addlestone Open University grafitti class 'as gone to ze Great Wall in China to gain international experience, and ze Tattoo-ologists 'ave gone to ze Costa Brava to practise on bronze skin as part of zer subsidized Common Market acclimatization programme. Unfortunately, we hear on Addlestone Radio zat some of ze more enthusiastic students 'ave been arrested by ze Spanish police for gang tattooing a young lady on ze beach. No matter, Addlestone relaxes and recovers its strength for ze autumn as ze rain washes ze pretty cottages and quaint streets, day after day after day. I 'ope Rod ze Roof returns from ze Club Med in Scarborough very soon. Ze roof is leaking again. But I can enjoy my bucket once more wizout feeling guilty.

At ze end of ze month we receive a postcard from Kev and Rodge. It is a typical disgusting French card such as my grandmother used to sell in 'er newsagent's shop in Canadel, showing a vulgar cartoon of a grinning naked couple wrapped around each other, floating in ze sea, wiz ze big-busted girl saying 'Would you like to eat my *Iles Flottantes?*' I make a note to start my autumn lectures wiz an explanation zat *îles flottantes* is a very refined French gourmet dessert.

SEPTEMBER

September in Addlestone, and ze village returns to life. Everybody is back from zer 'olidays, looking forward to collecting ze Giro cheque again. Ze streets are full of bicycles, and from our window we 'ear once more ze joyous sounds of Addlestone children's voices as zey pass, using ze local dialect – 'Effing and Blinding' I think it is called. Ze aroma from ze old Gutterspew factory once again tickles our oldfactory senses as we enjoy our traditional English breakfast of stewed prunes, All-Bran, Celtic Porridge Oats wiz milk and honey, and bacon and eggs wiz fried bread, washed down wiz orange juice and strong black coffee. I do 'ope Rod can fit our Turkish loo soon, otherwise we shall 'ave to change our diet.

Kev and Rodge arrive at ze bus station at six p.m., so Absinthe and I go to meet zem. Zey descend from ze coach looking very tired, so I invite zem for a livener at ze Dog and Duck. I notice zat zey do not 'ave zer 'doctor's' black bag wiz zem. Rodge explains zat it was stolen from zer tent on ze campsite and zey eventually got it back from ze French police, but ze contents were worn out and useless.

'But did you 'ave a good time?' I ask.

'Cosmic!' Rodge doesn't 'esitate. 'Absolutely Jurassic!'

Kev 'as revived now after 'is fifth Gutterspew: 'Did we 'ave a good time, Froggie Ash! I can't tell you! Boy, did I score, me old brave! I should play for England!'

'What did you win, Kev?' I ask naively.

'Everything in sight, mon matelot: Swedes, Ities, Sour-krouts, Frogspawn – you name it. Practically the whole United Nations! Great shame we lost the doctor's bag. I was fair worn out. But I tell you one thing, mon petit Frogman, you Frenchies haven't a clue about nosh 'n' booze. I'd have pawned my gold chain for some soggie Chinese take-away chips and a pint of warm ale. As far as I'm concerned, French cuisine's a load of old boules. Don't you dare invite me to that French Rude Brothers restaurant!'

'Ze touble is, Kev,' I try to explain, 'you 'ave ze sophisticated taste of an Addlestone gastronome.'

'Gastronome, mon brave? I've dozens of them at the bottom of my garden!' 'E and Rodge break into ze guffaw and nudge routine, so I stand well clear and ask: 'But were you able to use any of my French?'

'We 'ad to cancel it, Ash, I'm afraid,' Rodge answers. 'Every time we 'ad a go we got our faces slapped, and nothing occurred with the young ladies. So we stuck to Addlestonian sign language.' 'E lifted 'is open fist to 'is mouth and shook it rapidly.

'I don't know, Rodge,' Kev chips in, 'I picked up a word or two in the sleeping bag. For example: *entente cordiale* – a drink on the camp-site; *La-vie en rose* – a pink bathroom suite; *lune de miel* – you're nuts, honey; *belle de jour* – have a nice day; *condominium* – a house of ill repute; and *mais oui* – I think I need a loo.'

I explode wiz delight: 'Kev, you 'ave become such a scholar!' Absinthe claps 'er hands and gives Kev, and Rodge, a kiss on ze cheeks.

'Any chance of a sleeping-bag scholarship, Ash?' Kev tries to keep a straight face while trying not to spill 'is seventh pint.

'Anyway, Professor Mange-Tout,' Rodge gives me 'is Addlestonian mega wink, 'we've brought you two back a very special gift from the South of France. Voylà!'

And out of one of ze plastic bags, 'e produces a pink rubber Eiffel Tower. 'Ash and Absent, this is truly cosmic. The works, I guarantee you. We tested it of course, but we've washed it thoroughly afterwards so you don't need to fear for nothing. It's totally sanitized and computerized – as many mega-bytes as the missus wants.' Mega-winks and grins from Rodge and Kev.

'There's a little switch under here.' 'E points to ze base of ze tower. 'It takes Duracell LR6 AA batteries. Last for months unless you get carried away! So you can take it easy on the vitamins, Ash, me old Frog!'

Absinthe cannot take 'er eyes off ze tower and I deliver our thanks. 'Rodge, Kev, Absinthe and I are deeply honoured to receive zis beautiful memento of our dearly beloved France. It is so artistic, and quite a novel interpretation of ze Eiffel Tower such as I 'ave never seen before. It shall 'ave pride of place in our cottage. Shall we put it on ze mantlepiece in ze living room, ma petite poub?' I turn to Absinthe.

'It might be 'andier in our room upstairs, mon petit chou-fleur.' She looks at me wiz wide eyes.

Rodge and Kev are in uncontrollable laughter again: 'Stick it on the mantlepiece in the livin' room! You are a card, Ash tray!'

After another two hours of gaudy reminiscences and multiple Spews, we are all tired and go our separate ways. I tell Absinthe I 'ad no intention of putting ze tower on public display, I was just being polite. I 'ave never seen such a monstrous artefact in my 'ole life, but Absinthe disagrees.

It is Sunday, and ze day of ze annual Zimmerframe Marathon, which traditionally takes place in ze Co-op car park. Twenty-six laps, wiz only four five-minute stops allowed for a cup of tea. Ze trolley park 'as been cleared to make a pit lane, which is attended by Age Concern in full uniform, together wiz St John's Ambulance. Apparently, zis year zer is a difference, because Wally Connall 'as arranged for all ze pilots to be sponsored: each frame is plastered wiz publicity stickers and ze participants carry slogans on zer tee shirts. Bruiser Reade's grandad is sponsored by Gutterspew and 'is tee shirt carries 'Spew Extra Tonight!'. Kev's wife's mum, Doll, is sponsored by ze Women's Institute in collaboration wiz Ad Lib, ze Addlestone Liberation Front, wiz ze tee shirt slogan 'Ban Man!'. Granny Sleet is sponsored by Akimbos, and Rod's grandad, Bert, by ze Addlestone sewage works, wiz ze slogan 'Never Knowingly Passed'.

But ze surprise of ze day is ze appearance of Granny Berry, wiz 'er revolutionary new aerodynamic Racing Frame, which she 'as just got from ze National Health. It is very streamlined, and carries stickers from Bangers & Smash Motors. In yesterday's practice trial, Granny Berry did ze fastest lap, in 26 minutes, 49.27 seconds, and takes pole position. Ze weather is dry at ze moment but rain threatens so all ze frames are using normal hard rubber pads, but zey may 'ave to change mid-race to specially grooved wet-weather pads if zer is a downpour, to disperse ze water and give a better grip.

Ze race starts promptly at 10 a.m. as ze Marshall, Andy Lyons from ze Taxi Tavern, flicks on 'is cigarette lighter. Ze race develops into a vicious duel between Granny Berry and Rod's grandad, Bert, who are sworn lifelong enemies. Zer frames clash on many bends and zer are several shunts, but ze big drama comes when zey go into ze pits to change rubber pads, Granny

Berry just in front. She is out in 6 minutes, 4.31 seconds but Bert is out in 5 minutes, 59.63 seconds, and takes ze lead. On ze final bend Granny overtakes Bert on ze inside, but Bert puts on a spurt and cuts in front of 'er. Bert nearly loses it again by driving wiz only one 'and on ze frame and gesturing behind 'im wiz ze other – 'ighly unprofessional, Kev tells me, but Bert takes ze chequered hanky one length in front of Granny Berry. Ze crowd goes wild, especially ze Addlestone sewage works team. Bert wins in a record time of 8 hours, 57.29 seconds, but Granny Berry 'as ze fastest lap wiz 'er racing model. On ze wooden crate podium kindly lent by ze Co-op, Bert sprays 'imself and ze runners-up wiz a bottle of Guinness which 'e shakes as 'ard as 'is arthritis will allow, and zen receives 'is glittering prize of a three-tone 'orn to fix on 'is Zimmerframe, so 'e can let everybody know when 'e is coming. What an 'appy man, and what a well-deserved victory in gruelling conditions!

In celebration we all retire to ze Dog and Duck to toast Bert's success. Even Rod's wife, 'Cleave', who never got on wiz Bert because 'e was on ze 'Miss Cleavage' judging panel two years ago and voted against 'er when she was elected unanimously by ze other judges – even Cleave brings 'erself to congratulate 'im in front of ze cameras, so as to appear later on ze front page of ze *Addlestone Strumpet*. What a kind and forgiving lady.

Ze Zimmerframe Dooh-Daah band 'as been brought in specially for ze occasion. But zey 'ave changed zer presentation under zer new band-leader, a charming Irishman wiz ze gift of ze gob called Phil O'San. Now zey play tuneful music, pop and folk. Phil has distributed round ze bar a list of songs which can be requested: 'Just Zimmerframing in the rain'; 'We're all going on a Zimmer Holiday'; 'These Frames were made for walking'; 'Zimmerframe on by'; 'Zimmerframe on the wild side'; 'Zimmerframe Tall'; 'Zimmerframing back to Happiness'; 'In the Zimmer-Time'.

What a wonderful pop selection! Ze drivers dance ze night away, strangely wizout using zer Zimmerframes. I 'ope zey will not be injured, especially since Bert, who is doing ze valetta and tango wiz Granny Sleet, 'as now qualified for ze national finals, ze NCP Tour of Britain, to be 'eld next month in ze Lake District, an even more gruelling challenge, wiz steep mountain car parks and timed sprints across open motorways.

Tomorrow is ze birthday of Kev's mother-in-law, Doll. She will be seventy-six so, despite Kev's 'atred of her, Absinthe and I decide to give 'er a little memento from France at ze party Mave 'as arranged in ze Taxi Tavern. (Kev refuses to entertain 'er in ze 'oly of 'olies, ze Dog and Duck, because of 'is macho councillor image.) We take a string of fresh garlic bulbs that we 'ave been keeping in ze cellar. Doll smokes two packets of cigarettes a day, so we think ze garlic may 'elp ze ecological balance and ze ozone hole over Addlestone.

When we get to ze Taxi Tavern, ze place is full of Kev's friends, who 'e 'as bribed wiz ze offer of a free drink to come along to impress Doll, because apparently she 'as a small fortune under 'er mattress, and Kev is 'oping for a reconciliation. But after several Spews, Kev's diplomatic nature is overtaken by 'is hostile emotions. 'E calls for silence and wishes 'is mother-in-law Happy Birthday wiz all ze sincerity of an undertaker sympathizing wiz ze corpse's family. Wiz full pomp and circumstance Kev presents 'is white-haired mum-in-law wiz not one, but several gifts.

'Doll,' 'e begins between gritted teeth, 'on this suspicious occasion of your seventy-sixth summer, I bring gifts for your future happiness. First: here is a certificate, which I have bought for you at great expense,' 'e winks at ze guests. 'This certificate entitles you to free life–membership of the Addlestone Euthanasia Society, which I hope will be most useful to you.

'Secondly, I have arranged for you to break the habit of a life-time and become a benefactor to mankind – sorry, womankind! I give you three donor cards so that your glorious body will not fall off this mortal coil without maximum benefit to the younger generation. By these cards you magnanimously agree that your vital organs, immediately after your decease, may be ripped out and donated to save the life of another woman-being in dire need of a transplant. Of course, only your most vital organs will be taken. The first card is for your tongue; the second is for your lips; and the third is for your piles. We all believe these are your most vital and vigorous organs to donate to posterity. I'm sure, Dolly, you will be honoured to sign these cards and accompany-ing certificates for the future benefit of womankind.'

Kev just manages to get to ze exit before Doll's pint of Spew reaches 'im in a violent spray. Doll announces to ze giggling throng zat she will never accept such gifts from 'er no-good son-in-law. 'Owever, she will accept ze Euthanasia certificate in case she ever 'as to meet 'im again. And she will sign a donor card for 'er gusset regions, so zat 'er son-in-law can 'ave a transplant any time 'e wants, from whichever part is relevant. And wiz zat speech, she swings 'er fox fur round 'er neck and storms out of ze pub in 'igh dungeon, to ze applause of all ze women in ze pub and ze boos of ze men. What strong stock ze men and women of Addlestone come from! I think it must be ze free-range powdered eggs and rationing zey 'ad during ze War. Kev is not seen for several days, but when 'e does appear, 'e is wearing dark glasses, which do not quite cover ze purple bruises on 'is face.

Zer is no peace for Kev, because ze Runnynose Council 'as insisted on a vote about Addlestone's entry into ze Common Market. A few months ago Kev was elected councillor on an anti-Europe platform. But since ze visit of Italian film director Frederico Fellatini's beautiful daughter, Peccata Cardinale, and ze eventful 'oliday in St Tropez, Kev 'as been totally converted to Europe and ze Single Market. 'E plans an important speech at ze next Runnynose Council meeting which 'is opponents want to use to take Addlestone out of Europe – despite ze fact zat zey 'ave already independently joined ze ERM wiz zer new currency, ze Addle Stone.

But ze opposition is fierce: Mayor Roakes and ze 'ole council still want Addlestone to be completely independent of Westminster, but now zey even want to take Addlestone out of ze ERM. But Kev 'as a trump card. For years Addlestone 'as been trying to get twinned wiz a European town, or even part of a town, but 'as never found a willing partner. It 'as been rejected by towns all over Europe, including ze slums of Piraeus and Naples and ze red-light districts of Paris, Amsterdam and Hamburg. In desperation, ze council looked further afield but were rejected even by Beirut, Chernobyl and Sarajevo. But at last, through secret negotiations, Kev 'its ze jackpot: Maastricht accepts willingly in a desperate attempt to make friends wiz ze British people.

Zis is a great personal triumph for Kev, which 'e tells me of in confidence – 'e plans to make a surprise announcement at ze next council meeting. I am not sure it will swing ze vote for 'im. Anyway, Absinthe and I will go to ze meeting next week to 'ear ze debate – provided, zat is, Absinthe is not tied up wiz ze Women's Institute where she seems to spend many late evenings zese days. She always takes ze Eiffel Tower wiz 'er to show 'er friends, and always returns wiz lots of Addle Stones. It must be very boring, but if she is 'appy . . .

Sunday is Harvest Festival at ze Free Range church, and ze animals arrive wiz sheaves of wheat and bales of hay strapped to zer backs. We all sing 'When Hops Are Safely Gathered In' followed by 'Let's Go To The Hop' to ze accompaniment of Trev ze Rev on electric guitar.

After delivering a moving sermon, Trev ze Rev leads us into what 'e calls ze final 'person-song', which I do not understand, but Rod ze Roof in ze pew behind whispers 'sotted voce' zat it is a new definition adopted by ze Runnynose synod as ze least sexist alternative to 'hymns' and 'hyrrhs', which 'ave caused so much internecine warfare in clerical ranks during recent months. Ze Free Range church is very progressive. Not only are women to be ordained but even ze animals will be allowed to participate. Ze cows will provide fresh milk for ze single parents' afternoon tea meetings and ze Lord's prayer will be read in dog Latin. As Eric Surplice says when Absinthe and I leave ze church, 'In today's world we must open our hearts and minds to animals and women.'

After lunch, Absinthe and I go for a spin in our volvo estate round ze local countryside. Absinthe takes Polaroids – because she is so impetuous – of ze electric pylons and ze gasometers. We stop on ze bridge over ze M25 to take a picture of ze latest contraflow and all ze cars parked along it. Zen we drive past ze local farm, which runs a car–boot sale every Sunday morning. Outside, above ze hedge at ze side of ze road, is a big sign, 'Noses – Pick your own'. Absinthe thinks it must be a typo but I'm not so sure.

In ze evening, I go to ze Dog and Duck to meet Kev in ze Snug and help 'im wiz 'is speech on Europe for ze council meeting next Tuesday. Unfortunately, ze Snug is crowded out wiz ze terrible twins, Torvill and Dean, Kylie and Erin and zer friends, playing poker for Smarties. We discover later zat ze Smarties are being distributed by Dean at 50p each.

Kev and I take refuge in ze Coq au Vin which is quieter. I ask 'im why did 'e really convert from being a pure Addlestonian to an international Europhile.

'I tell you, Ash matelot,' Kev explains, sucking from 'is bottle of Spew Extra wiz a slice of beetroot on ze neck, 'I was converted like Paul on the road to damnation. It came to me in a blinding flash as I was chatting up this Swedish bird on the Pamplemousse nudy beach at St Tropez. Why do we have to be so racist? Why discriminate between races. We're all beautiful people. We all love each other – we all want uniting together. No man is an island, not even Britain. All the birds I chatted up down there agreed they should be united with the Brits. It's my personal crusade now, Euro-Ash.'

We work through ze evening and several Spew Extras, as I try to focus Kev's mind on political rather zan emotional arguments.

Tuesday arrives and Absinthe and I go down to ze First Addlestone Brownie Nissan Hut Hall to attend ze vital council meeting. As we arrive we see a line of demonstrators, including Kev's wife, Mave, and 'is fierce mum-in-law, Doll, 'olding high a banner – 'Don't be Mass-Tricked'. Obviously, zer 'as been a leak about ze twinning result. Inside ze hall, ze attendance is very thin, which is not surprising because it is Flingo night at ze Bingo Hall, and ze Dog and Duck is running its Happy Hour: one free Gutterspew for every ten pints drunk wizin ze hour.

Ze council on ze platform is set-faced. Mayor Cliff Roakes is symbolically wearing a black suit and black tie. Kev is going to 'ave a tough job. But 'e rises to ze occasion.

'Ladies, Gentlemen, and fellow Europeans,' Kev begins, 'lend me your Walkmans. To be a European or not to be, that is the question. Britain is no island. Our glorious thoroughbred nation has always opened its arms to the world: the Romans, the Vikings, the Normans, the Irish navvies, the West Indian bus drivers, the Pakistani newsagents, the Aussie Page Three artists, the Czech pension fund managers, the Japanese industrial philanthropists – you name it.

'We have always been a cosmopolitan nation, conquering the world and inviting the world to conquer us. We've taught the world fair play: cricket, football, darts, shove ha'penny, tiddly-winks, snap. No matter that we can't win any of these games any more: we are the greatest losers the world has ever known.

'Let's have no talk of the unelected bureaucrats in Brussels: if our disproportionately representative members of the House of Commons are crushed by Brussels, never fear: our unelected House of Lords will out-unelect anybody in Brussels. Our lack of constitution and our monarchy is our strength. We have nothing to fear from Europe except our own xenophobia. Let us go forward into the sunlit uplands of the European dream with hearts of oak – for St George, St Crispin and the DSS!

'Finally, as a token of Europe's good faith in our beloved village, the most important city in Europe has deigned to be twinned with Addlestone: from the very hub-bub of Europe, no lesser city than Maastricht itself!' Kev waves a piece of paper above 'is head. 'Ladies, gentlemen and fellow Europeans, I present to you the twinning certificate signed by the Mayor of Maastricht!'

Kev flops, exhausted into 'is deck-chair to ze applause of ze three white-rinse ladies in ze front row, but, alas, ze council rejects Kev's plea by six votes to one and opts for a referendum on Addlestone's independent membership of ze European Community, confident zat ze citizenry will overwhelmingly vote to take Addlestone out of ze Single Market. But at least we 'ave one more chance to persuade ze people of zer best interests.

Absinthe and I congratulate Kev on 'is speech and take 'im to ze Dog and Duck to lick our wounds. Rodge is convinced zat ze only way to win is to take ze male councillors to St Tropez (without wives of course) and zey'll be converted overnight, but Kev points out ze council coffers can't stretch to zat unless we can find a sponsor. It is agreed I should try wiz ze local travel agent, Nadir Tours, whose slogan is 'Escape From It All – one-way tickets our speciality'. I will see zem tomorrow.

On ze way 'ome we call in at Addlestone's newest late-night fast-food emporium, which Trev ze Rev 'as enterprisingly opened next to ze Free Range crypt. It is called 'The Last Supper Take-Away', and specializes in Communionburgers wiz tomato ketchup, rapidly renamed 'Commyburgers'. Back at Station Approach zey taste delicious washed down wiz several Bloody Maries. Just as we retire a huge thunderclap lights up ze railway sidings and a noisy deluge follows. I look forward to 'aving ze bucket in ze bed again.

Next day, ze *Addlestone Strumpet* is delivered wiz an amazing front-page headline: 'Humanitarian Aid Reaches Addlestone!' Apparently, Phnom Pen Nib, ze proprietor of ze Pol Pot Pourri, 'as arranged for 'is compatriots in Cambodia to send food parcels to ze needy in Addlestone who cannot survive on zer Giro Cheques, or do not even qualify to receive zem! Zis is a miracle.

I race down ze Dog and Duck to ask 'ow it works. Rodge and ze Brain are zer, taking zer 'elevenses' as zey call it – zer eleventh pint of ze day. Zey explain ze good news. Because of ze Giro Cheque famine, Kev 'as negotiated a relief package from Cambodia, consisting of Cambodian frozen giant slugs, fried scorpions and a special local delicacy, ladies fingers. Ze twelve laden trucks from Cambodia 'ave travelled seven thousand miles across swamps and deserts to bring zis aid to our grateful villagers.

Ze trucks roll over ze level crossing at midday precisely and are directed by our traffic warden, Jeff Clampit, to ze Runnynose Council car park, outside Mayor Roakes' parlour. Mayor Cliff insists on controlling ze distribution under 'is strict supervision to avoid any misappropriation of zese valuable supplies. Surprisingly, very few people seem to qualify for ze Mayor's distribution programme which is restricted to ze most needy. Luckily, Absinthe and I qualify for one frozen slug each, but many are turned away. Mayor Roakes announces zat a reserve will be kept in ze council deep freeze to tide us over ze winter months. 'Ow thoughtful 'e is. Absinthe and I eat our slugs wiz garlic butter on a bed of ladies fingers which, as a special delicacy, ze council 'as allowed to be sold off for ze profit of ze Addlestone Crochet Society. Washed down wiz a bottle of Mr Phnom Pen Nib's best Sang Rouge wine it is a delicious dish.

Strangely, in ze next few days ze gardens of Addlestone are invaded by giant slugs, which devour flowers and vegetables at a voracious rate. But luckily, ze local garden centre, run by Cliff Roakes' sister Twiggie, advertises a giant slug-killer, which is very expensive but is very effective and is a sell-out.

It is Sunday again. 'Ow time flies when you are busy! We are treated to another of Trev ze Rev's immaculate sermons, zis week on ze new Free Range version of ze Ten Commandments, skilfully adapted for ze congregation of peasants and animals. Trev, who 'as spent a lot of time in ze Antipodes, preaches ze virtue of being kind to animals and ze sin of adultery. As 'e intones 'Thou shalt not covert thy neighbour's ewe' some of ze sheep cry. We drop a couple of Addle Stones on ze plate and leave church spiritually refreshed, but unfortunately ze sermon 'as not reached ze parts Gutterspew can reach, so we hurry to ze pub.

Rodge is zer, wiz six pints lined up on ze bar in front of 'im, which, he says, is to save queueing all ze time. 'E is going to spend ze afternoon at ze cricket club when ze Dog and Duck closes, because zer bar is open all afternoon. Rodge is astonished when 'e learns zat Absinthe and I 'ave never yet been to a cricket match, so at closing time 'e insists on taking us down ze club. Ze match takes place on ze Addlestone football ground because it is ze only green space available, but ze centre of ze pitch 'as been clipped down by Twiggie Roakes' garden centre shears.

Ze game 'as started when we arrive. Rodge tells us it is a very important match because ze visiting team is ze hated St Hillian's club, who 'ave ze distinction of once fending off an Australian touring side, to be defeated by only an innings and 953 runs to rival ze England record. Rodge, who 'as ordered more pints, tries somewhat incoherently to explain ze rules of ze game, but I cannot grasp all ze ins and outs.

Addlestone loses ze toss and is put in to bat. Ze batsmen 'ave borrowed zer 'elmets and mouthshields from ze shove ha'penny team but, Rodge explains, 'sotted voce' so Absinthe cannot 'ear, zey cannot afford cartons (I zink 'e says) to protect zer tender regions. Rodge thinks it is a blessing in disguise, because it makes zem defend zer wickets wiz greater vigour, especially to avoid being 'out BBW', whatever that is.

Rodge continues, 'I've told the Club President, Bernie Pire, he should recommend it to the England selectors. We wouldn't half save a few wickets against the Aussie bowlers that way.'

I notice also zat ze referees each 'ave a large black dog on a leash, and ze fielders are all carrying mobile phones, so I ask Rodge ze meaning of zis.

'Well, Ash me silly short leg, the St Hillians are a load of old yuppies who can't function without one hand on a mobile phone, even in bed, so they've been accepted as legal as a special dispensation. They use them sneakily to talk to each other without our lot hearing anything. And since there are more droopies than yuppies in their side, the captain can phone them up and give them a good bollicking when they fall asleep in the long grass.

'As for the umpires' Rotweilers, that was imposed on us by the County Court after last year's internecine fiasco. What happened was, Bernie Pire, last year's captain, who hates the St Hillians' guts because they never use his funeral services, sayin' he's too common to embalm their aristocratic corpses – Bernie got the hump during the Hillians' innings because they were scoring mercilessly off his bowling: fours and sixes off every ball except when Bernie was deliberately throwing wides. So when the Hillians' captain, Chas Dearlove, was just about to hit the winning stroke, Bernie runs in to bowl but doesn't release the ball, he gallops down the crease at full tilt straight at Chas, smashes him in the face with the ball, shouting "Another St Hillian for the crematorium!" snatches the bails off the stumps and races off with them to the pavilion, where he downs a couple of swift Babychams. Fighting breaks out on the pitch as the two teams lay into each other. The match has to be abandoned, and Bern is hauled in front of the committee charged with grievous bodily bowling and banned from drinking at the club bar until next Sunday. Henceforth, it was decreed that the umpires should have Rotweilers on the field to deter any future violence.'

Rodge returns to 'is pints and we all fall asleep in our deckchairs. We are awakened by a sudden downpour and everybody, including ze players, gratefully race for ze bar, where I am introduced to Bern Pire. Naive as ever, I ask him 'ow it is zat ze English invented a game zat can take up to five days in ze open air in such a rainy climate. Bern explains zat ze British Empire was built on cold showers on and off ze playing fields of Eton. Ze game continues fitfully between downpours. Addlestone are 34 all out and St Hillians go in to bat. Addlestone's white-haired fielders may not 'ave mobile phones, but many 'ave souped-up electric wheel-chairs so zey can chase St Hillians' many boundary hits.

Rapidly zer score reaches 33 for no wicket but ze day is saved by one final, prolonged cloud burst which forces a draw. Bern Pire gives me a beer-spilling nudge: 'Now you know, Monsieur Blancmange-Tout, why we play in the monsoon season, laughingly called Summer. At least the rain gives us a chance to draw when there's no hope of winning!'

I cannot understand why ze British consider a draw a victory. Perhaps winning is not thought of as fair play.

At seven o'clock, official opening time, we retire to ze Dog and Duck to celebrate our victory. As Sharon opens ze doors to let us in, we find Kev and Rod already installed and on zer second Spew. Rod assures me ze Turkish loo and bidet will be delivered zis week and ze roof tiles are already 'on their way'. Kev is in a high state of excitement, which I initially take to be inebriation, because ze referendum on Europe and Maastricht has been announced for Thursday week.

'Gonna need your speechifying help again, me old bon mot.' Kev offers us a round of pints. Rodge, not known for 'is love of ze Europeans, unless zey're under twenty-five and wearing monokinis, launches in.

'Trouble with you, Kev, you've got Chunnel vision. I'd rather be dictated to by the House of Lords than the gastro-gnomes of Zurich and Brussels. Telling us what ingredients we can and can't put in our custard toasties and mushy-pea burgers. You don't stand a chance, Kev. Give in gracefully I say. In any case, I've heard on the grapevine your missus and her mum, Doll, are mounting a dirty tricks campaign against you, backed by the hard-liners on the Council. They're saying you've sold drinking straws to Somalia for conversion into blow-pipes!'

Rodge gives me a giant wink and almighty nudge zat sends me flying across ze lino, straight into ze Ladies – a good shot! As I pick myself up off ze seat, I notice zey 'ave installed new condom machines selling an exciting new brand, 'Muckers', in various flavours: 'Liquorice All-Sorts', 'Pineapple-on-a-Stick' and 'Kum-Quat'. But alas, no Pernod or Roquefort.

Back at ze bar, Kev continues 'is losing battle against ze Europhobes. At ze end of a rowdy and abusive evening wiz stonebats flying, Kev pulls me to one side and slurs deafeningly into my ear zat 'e's been able to use 'is influence to get ze DSS to consider my Giro Cheque application. How wonderful! Absinthe and I bid good night and meander back to Station Approach, looking forward to ze busy week ahead.

RODGE THE DODGE

OCTOBER

Z e seasons are changing and ze nights are drawing in. Zer is a distinct pinch in ze air, ze sleeveless shirts 'ave disappeared, and zer is 'ardly a tattoo in sight. Suddenly, one morning ze *Addlestone Strumpet* carries ze headline 'Her Maj Uses The F-word!'.

Ze leader announces zat ze Queen 'as entered ze F-word Hall of Fame by being taped while speaking off ze record before a TV interview. Addlestone Radio investigative factotum, Jerry Logan, 'as obtained a secret copy and plays ze tape over ze Addlestone airwaves. Her Maj was about to be interviewed about ze recession and Britain's growing unemployed, but off ze record she is 'eard to say zat 'er government is a 'bunch of f****** merchant bankers', which I cannot quite understand, because I thought government ministers couldn't take top jobs in ze City until after zey 'ad been thrown out of office. Absinthe and I are highly amused to discover Her Maj is one of us, but ze Dog and Duck is up in arms.

'She has no right to hijack the language of the common man,' Rodge fumes. 'It belongs to us, it's our hereditage and progative. How can we get full effect out of our limited education if the aristocracy start making swearing respectable? If it becomes an upper-class pastime we'll all have to pay to go into the Royal Enclosure or the Royal Opera before we can say "F-off". Why can't the Queen stick to her own expelletives, like "balderdash!" and "jolly bad hockey stick!" and leave us in peace? It's a diabolical insult to the working man.'

'Or, in the case of Addlestone, the non-working man!' Kev chips in wiz a giant wink and a nudge I am getting quite good at dodging – although I enjoy my unplanned trips into ze Ladies. But ze Brain, who 'as been coughing and slurping 'is beer through 'is rolled cigarette at ze bar, perks up.

'Maybe I could make so bold as to offer a possible solution to this constitutional crisis?' Ze whole pub waits wiz bated glasses. 'Might I suggest that we hold a contest to find the best new swear-words which we can use without the establishment knowing anything about them.' Ze Brain pauses to relight 'is soggy cigarette. 'Of course we'll only need to choose two: one verb and one noun. And they can only have four letters. We can have different categories of entry, for the under-fives and over-eighties for example, just to give everyone a fair chance. And of course you can make up new words, as long as they sound dirty.'

Ze pub 'ails ze Brain's brilliant idea. It is agreed zat Jasper Meiggs should be asked to administer ze vote to ensure fair play, – 'e 'as never used a four-letter word in 'is life so 'e'll be completely objective. Zen Kev 'as a brainwave: why not get all ze nominations in and make a short list which can be put on ze back of ze Maastricht referendum voting slips. Everybody is agreed but no time can be lost because ze referendum is due in ten days.

Absinthe and I retire to Station Approach for a nightcap of Cornish Pastis and ze delicious traditional British dish of canned spaghetti in tomato sauce wiz 'NO ADDED SUGAR'. We are relieved because ze ingredients on ze label list twenty-five types of saccharine and artificial sweetener, so natural sugar is unnecessary. Absinthe decides, in a brilliant stroke of genius, to make a tomato spaghetti meringue to utilize all ze artificial sugar. It is a fantastic success: after one hour in ze oven ze meringues come out crispy pink, packed tight wiz scrumptious spaghetti strands. We will eat zem tomorrow after cooling zem in ze freezer. Tonight ze Cornish Pastis is satisfaction enough.

At eight next morning we are awoken by a loud hammering on ze front door. Unbelievably, it is Rod and 'is team, who 'ave brought ze correct 'châtaigne d'eau' Turkish loo and bidet. Absinthe and I are ecstatic. Finally ze luxury of motional release in traditional French comfort!

Rod and 'is mates burst into ze kitchen and commandeer ze crate of Spew Extra lager I 'ave been keeping in ze cellar in ze vain 'ope zey will eventually do ze work zey 'ave been promising for so long. Ze colour is not ze same as 'marron glacé', but zer is no problem if Absinthe goes easy on ze curry.

By midday ze old toilet bowl 'as been removed and is lying in ze front yard wiz ze new equipment. Rod 'as promised zat ze new loo and bidet will be installed and fully operational by nightfall so zat Absinthe and I can 'ave our take-away Tandoori without fear. Zere is a lot of hammering and dust as zey prepare ze toilet and ze plumbing for fitment. Absinthe and I take a break at midday to visit ze bank and draw out money to be sure we can pay Rod at ze end of ze day.

English banks are quite amazing. It is not even necessary to queue inside ze bank to draw out money: everybody can queue outside in ze pouring rain to take money from ze cash dispenser in ze wall. To ensure zat customers draw their money quickly, zere is no canopy over ze dispenser to protect you from ze rain, so everybody moves very fast. 'Ow ze English love zer refreshing rain! I am very happy to 'ave opened my account at ze Deaf-and-Dumb Bank for Handicapped Investors, whose motto is 'Nice Business To Do People With'. If you 'ave a problem wiz ze bank zey take away all ze hassle by keeping you informed by letters, which are conveniently deducted from your account automatically at a nominal charge of only seventy pounds. What sophistication computers 'ave brought into our 'umble lives.

I am also impressed by ze British Telecom system, which provides special outdoor fresh-air booths on every street, making sure zat nobody spends more zan one minute on ze phone because ze traffic noise makes it impossible to 'ave a long conversation.

Absinthe and I 'ave a jam-butty burger at ze Taxi Tavern for a change. Because of ze recessionary slump, ze competition for Giro Cheque beer vouchers is now very fierce in our village, so the pubs are rivalling each other to attract all ze Giro Cheque holders. Ze Taxi Tavern is offering 'Beer Miles': a free pint wiz every hundred yards of ale consumed on ze premise – but invalidated if any of ze yards are regurgitated wizin spitting distance of ze pub. Absinthe and I manage to clock up a mile and a half before 'elping each other back to Station Approach.

It is now late afternoon and we return 'ome to find ze cottage in complete chaos and hubbub. Dust and swear-words (old-fashioned royal-style) fill ze air. We offer Rod and 'is team another crate of Spew Extra, and Rod explains ze problem is bigger zan 'e originally thought. 'E is not sure to finish by nightfall after all, so we may 'ave to make alternative toilet arrangements overnight. Zis is very embarrassing, because we do not get on well wiz our neighbours. Ze problem is zat as French people we 'ave been totally misunderstood.

It is of course all Absinthe's fault. I am terrified of spiders but Absinthe will not allow me to kill zem. Whenever we find one, I jump on ze nearest chair while Absinthe whistles to it, delicately

97

picks it up wiz a sheet of soft toilet tissue and gently throws it out of ze bathroom window or ze front door to lead a new outdoor life. Unfortunately, our neighbours 'ave reported us to ze Council's Sanitary Department for throwing used toilet paper out of ze house instead of flushing it down ze loo. In Britain, apparently, it is not allowed to protect our furry eight-footed friends, only four-footed friends. What racist prejudice!

Ze neighbours on both sides give us ze cold elbow and refuse us access to zer sanitary facilities. I explain to Rod zat I refuse to use ze back garden and spoil ze dandelions and daisies, and in any case ze nettles might cause Absinthe an injury. Funny though, she came back wiz a rash from 'er last visit to ze WI – I didn't know zer were nettles inside ze First Brownie Nissen Hut Hall. But Rod, brilliant improviser zat 'e is, comes up wiz a marvellously practical solution: to use ze new self-flushing public pavement loo in ze High Street. Zis is brill because it reminds me of our pungently romantic pissoires in France, which were viciously ripped out by ze Green Party, forcing ze French nation to become rogue urinators just like Addlestone.

At five-thirty, Rod and 'is team leave ze mess behind zem, promising to return 'at first light tomorrow'. (I discover next day zat 'first light' is not dawn but ze first crate of Gutterspew light ale, which I 'ave to provide to oil ze wheels of British industry, as usual.) But, after Rod and 'is lads have gone, Absinthe and I 'ave to brave ze 'Pavvy Loo' in Addlestone High Street. Absinthe escapes wizout a scar, but when I 'ave finished inside I cannot find ze exit button. I press everything in sight to open ze door but no luck. In claustrophobic panic I press a red button and ze whole cubicle starts spraying me wiz violent jets of water: I 'ave activated ze monster's self-cleaning system. Finally, ze water sprays stop and ze door opens. I stagger out on to ze street soaked to ze skin. Passers-by look at me askance, obviously thinking I 'ave severely wet myself. I squelch back to Station Approach dripping wet, to peals of laughter from Absinthe, who never understands zat I am not a mechanic but a brilliant creative advertising man wiz no knowledge of technology.

We decide it is unsafe to drink too many Gutterspews zis evening, and a Tandoori take-away is definitely taboo until Rod 'as finished. So we stick to Entre Deux Merdes and Cornish Pastis until Wally Connall phones to invite us to ze Coq for a glass of wine wiz 'is mad inventor friend, Alan Stein. We turn up to find a short, fat dishevelled man, wiz long straggly grey 'air and moustache to match, wearing tiny, thick pebble glasses.

Wally makes ze introductions and Al explains, in a thick Russian accent, zat 'e is a rouble refugee from ze Soviet Disunion. I praise 'im for 'is ingenious toilet-roll dispenser and photo-chromatic contact lenses.

'But I am now verking on two new inventions that vill have even vider mass appeal.' Al is proud of 'is profession. 'Don't mind if I join you in another glass of champagne, comrade Mange-Tout?' 'E raises an empty glass and gives me a winning smile containing very few teeth. I am not drinking champagne, but it is such an 'onour to meet ze professor zat I order a bottle of Veuve Twankey.

'Apart from permanent recession, ze two greatest problems in ze verld today are masculine hygiene and rape, both of which are caused by ze male sexual organ, as Clement Freud discovered, as you may remember, during one of his famous vet dreams – you know he was a dog lover of course?' Professor Stein pauses to allow me to refill 'is glass again. 'Ze male sexual organ was designed first for sexual intercourse for which it is quite efficient, and secondly for urination for which it is a disaster, because it sprays like a shot-gun. Research among spouses in Addlestone has established that 66.74 per cent of ze spray misses ze toilet bowl completely. Ze percentage is as high as 99 per cent when ze male is drunk. Why does this not happen during sexual inter-course, you ask? I will tell you: because there is a funnel to challenge ze liquid!' Al pauses for another refill and time to let ze profundity of 'is analysis penetrate our humble minds.

'Taking a leaf out of ze female anatomy, I have invented and patented ze "P-Cone for men"! A special device made from soft abuser-friendly tissue in ze shape of a small funnel, which is placed over ze male organ prior to ze moment of urinatory ejaculation. Ze fluid is directed through ze hole at ze base of ze funnel, so that it comes out in a narrow stream that can be easily targeted into ze centre of ze toilet bowl, without a single drop making a mess!

'And then, vot is even more amazing, when ze ejaculation is finished, ze soft user-friendly tissue can be used to wipe ze male organ dry before flushing it ecologically down ze bowl, thus saving underpant corrosion and laundry bills. Of course macho Englishmen will find it difficult to swallow ze P-Cone concept as an infringement of their masculinity. So to launch ze idea I plan to give away a packet of three wiz every pack of three P-Cones.' Al leans back on ze bar to bask in ze glow of our universal admiration of 'is genius.

Unfortunately, Rodge, our Euro-Dodger, 'as come into ze bar and 'as been listening to Al's exposé.

'It'll never work, me old Ruski-roulette mate,' Rodge butts in. 'English men are not going to have their privates interfered with by modern technology, however abuser-friendly. No chance!'

But Rodge's is a lone voice: all ze women in ze pub – Rod's wife, Cleave, and Kev's family, Mave and Doll – heartily endorse Al's idea, and Wally Connall announces 'is advertising campaign slogan: 'You're Never Alone – With a P-Cone', based on ze marketing strategy of extended usage. Addlestone will be ze test market for zis brilliant new product, which Al tells us will be distributed alongside 'is toilet-roll dispensers in all ze Gents toilets in Addlestone. 'E pauses for another bottle of Twankey, which of course I offer because we are all so enthralled by 'is treatise. I ask 'im what is 'is second brill invention.

'You vill not believe zis. It is so simple and so perfect,' Al continues after several slurps. 'Why are there no more pretty young ladies walking ze streets at night for our delectation? I vill tell you. Because they are afraid of rape! So they stay at home wiz their mothers or husbands. I have therefore invented ze "Fanny-Clamp".

Made out of impregnable polystyrene, it is strapped around ze woman's nether regions and locked by my brilliant new patented device, ze "Computerized Universal Night Timer," which allows ze woman to set ze computerized timer on ze Fanny-Clamp until such time as she returns home to safety. If every woman in ze country wore zis device on ze street all rapists would be forced into ze DIY store!' Al takes another slurp pause. 'And for ze ultra nervous, I have a deluxe model wiz a screaming siren which can be heard several police stations away if interfered wiz. It is called ze "Kako-Fanny".'

We all congratulate Al on 'is amazing contributions to ze quality of Addlestone life. 'E points out zat 'e is, as 'e says, 'slur-pless', so I buy another bottle of Veuve Twankey; as Al says, zer's nothing like a bottle of Veuve to add life to a party.

Al explains ze Fanny-Clamp is going on sale in Addlestone next month by male order. 'E is importing zem from Bangkok where, 'e says, zey 'ave undergone ze most rigorous testing wiz, such great success zat ze Thai government 'ad to ban zem because zey were wiping out zer essential tourist industry.

At ze end of ze evening, we return to Station Approach and retire for a fitful night. Three times I have to race out in my silk dressing gown to relieve myself at ze Pavvy Loo – which is unfortunate, because it is blowing a gale wiz freezing rain to add ze icing to ze gingerbread. I shall never drink Veuve Twankey again – it gives 'Veuve' in ze wrong places.

Next morning at first 'Gutterspew light', Rod and ze 'Cleavage Boys', as I 'ave discovered zey are known around town (because of Rod's wife), arrive an hour before opening time. After more dust clouds, thickened by 'language', as Rodge calls it, and several crates of ze golden Gutterspew, while I hide in ze Dog and Duck and Absinthe goes off again to ze WI for a matinée, whatever zat is supposed to be (I don't care as long as she avoids ze nettles). Rod appears in ze bar and tells me ze toilet equipment is finally installed and ready for use. Quel miracle! I am so excited I rush off to ze Women's Institute to tell Absinthe we can squat at last in luxury, but she 'as apparently gone off wiz a colleague to demonstrate 'er Eiffel Tower to ze Mayor, Cliff Roakes, in 'is parlour at ze Runnynose Council offices next to ze Citizens' Advice Bureau skyscraper.

I go back 'ome, to find Rod and Co clearing up somewhat inefficiently. Rod suggests zat, after such major surgery, ze toilet needs a little redecoration.

'I can match your "shatin do" colour on the walls if you like it so much. Give it a nice glossy waterproof veneer – make it quite veneerial!' Rod gives me ze Addlestone mega-wink. 'Never know, Monsieur Fag-Ash, could enhance your love life! Never done it on a B-Day personally. Everywhere else mind you, but never on a B-Day. Could be quite a turn on with matching "shaton" walls. I could get a matching super-furry rug as well. Save your kneecaps if you need a bit of a change, know what I mean?'

I dodge 'is nudge just in time to avoid being catapulted into our beautiful new loo. I thank Rod for 'is kind advice and offer 'is boys a final crate of Spew Light before taking 'im aside to give 'im ze three thousand pounds I 'ad promised 'im at 'is special cash price.

What joy! At last, a perfect French toilet in a perfect rural English cottage. A squatters' paradise! Soon we are known around ze village as ze 'French Squitter Squatters': I do not knew what zis means, but we are honoured to be so recognized by ze local community. But I wish zey would recognize me for ze famous Addlestone Giro Cheque. Kev tells me I will 'ear very soon; ze same way Rod keeps telling me our roof tiles will arrive very soon.

On Saturday afternoon, Addlestone holds its traditional annual Wolf Whistling competition in ze High Street. Apparently, it dates back to ze days of ze Teddy Bear boys in ze Fifties, when all ze young men leant on street corners and whistled at ze girls going by. But now ze contest is strictly formalized and controlled. Ze male contestants take turns to hide in ze Oxfam doorway while ze judges – Mayor Roakes, Kev, and Rod's wife Cleave – sit outside ze Christian Bookshop cafe opposite sipping camomile tea. Kev says zis is to set an example but I know 'e 'as a 'ip flask in 'is denim pocket.

Each contestant 'as ten goes whistling at girls walking by (who know nothing of ze contest). Zey can choose any woman to whistle at as long as zey are over fifteen and not using a Zimmerframe. If ze girl pays no attention it is of course no points; if she pays some attention but carries on walking it is five points; if she stops and turns round it is ten points. Ze winner gets a paid night out wiz ze girl of 'is choice from ze ones who stopped for him. Which is 'ow Rod met Cleave when 'e got maximum points and chose 'er out of ze ten girls because, as 'e put it, she had ze 'biggest potentials'.

Ze signal is given for ze start and Rod's son, Dean, takes up 'is position in ze Oxfam doorway, hoping to rival 'is father's victory. 'E makes several brave attempts, wiz fingers down 'is throat, but to no success. But zen, on ze final try, a very beautiful young girl walks past, wearing a black, low-cut, see-through chiffon blouse and white skin-tight ski-pants. Dean let's rip wiz an almighty whistle zat can be heard ze length and breadth of ze High Street. Unfortunately, at ze same moment Granny Sleet shuffles by, but not using 'er Zimmerframe. Ze young girl walks straight on snub nose in ze air but Granny Sleet stops and looks round eagerly in ze direction of Oxfam. Dean suddenly breaks cover and sprints away at full tilt down ze High

Street, and is not seen by Rod and Cleave till nightfall. Neverthless, Dean could still win ze contest if no one else scores ten points.

'Owever, several of ze other contestants do score more, but not very highly. Maybe it is ze cold weather. Ze final contestant 'as to be called more zan once: eventually a bent, white-haired old man, wearing a deaf-aid, 'anging on to a shaking pint in one hand and 'olding 'is back wiz ze other, shuffles through ze crowd and manages to reach ze Oxfam doorway. Wally Connall whispers to me it is old Les 'ze Lech', who 'as laid fourteen wives to rest and is desperate for a fifteenth; 'e was Wolf Whistle champion three years running from 1973 to 1975, which won 'im three wives – twenty years ago when he was only seventy-three. Les is very fussy about ze girls 'e chooses to whistle at – nothing over ze age of twenty, it appears. 'E builds up a good score wiz several fives until Sharon from ze Dog and Duck swaggers past and stops, zen turns round wiz a smile, giving Les an extra ten points.

A rumour grows among ze spectators zat Les 'as offered financial incentives to some if not all ze girls after 'is recent pools win. At ze last whistle Les needs a clear ten points to win ze contest. At zat moment ze voluptuous young Cherry Flashit trips by, wearing a remarkably short micro-skirt given ze cool breeze, together wiz bright-scarlet tights and wobbly high heels. A rather exhausted, but nevertheless melodious, whistle struggles across ze air from ze doorway, but it is enough to stop Cherry in 'er tracks. She turns and walks back towards Oxfam wearing a wistful smile and little else. Les jumps out of ze doorway arms wide open gasping, 'My darling, at last!'

Cherry leaps back, screams in terror, turns and races across to ze Pavvy Loo where she locks 'erself in. Les hobbles after 'er, shouting 'Don't let her escape! She's mine! She's mine!' But 'e is restrained by ze committee and calms down after being offered a pint in ze Dog and Duck to celebrate 'is magnificent victory. Ze judges promise to find 'im another partner for 'is triumphant night out if Cherry cannot be persuaded.

At ze end of ze evening's celebration, Les is carried back by ze committee to 'is mobile home beside ze railway sidings just outside our bedroom window. A few days later, Cher Flashit agrees to go out wiz Les provided Nigel Bart is also invited as chaperon. She still carries a flashlight for 'im and believes zis will put Les off 'er stride. Ze committee accepts, but on ze night, to everyone's surprise, after ze candlelight supper in ze waiting area of ze Tandoori Take-Away, Cherry chooses to go back wiz Les to ze Mobile Home Park instead of Nigel's Rotweiler Mansion on St George's Hill. Strangely, Cherry is not seen about town for several days.

Ze day of ze referendum arrives, with ze balloting taking place in ze Free Range Church Hall. By a clever move on ze part of Trev ze Rev, 'e 'as made ze church car park 'Pray and Display', so zat every voter who comes by car 'as to contribute to ze church coffers. Kev 'as fought a furious, but I am sure 'opeless, battle to rally support for Europe. On my side, I failed to persuade Nadir Tours to take ze hardline councillors on a fact-finding trip to ze bottomless beaches of St Tropez, so everyone seems to be against 'im. In one last-ditch effort, Kev persuades ze *Addlestone Strumpet* to offer a return trip to Maastricht for only one Addle Stone for everyone who votes for Addlestone staying in Europe and ze ERM, but it excites very little interest, despite his showing everybody lurid photos of Maastricht's red light district. But Kev 'as even one more trump card: ze phrasing of ze question on ze ballot paper. In ze interests of fair play 'e 'as insisted on drafting ze question 'imself, 'to ensure no bias'.

Ze question reads: 'Are you in favour of Addlestone withdrawing from the ERM while remaining unilaterally in the European Community provided that the social chapter is handled by Westminster in accordance with the treaty of Rome and the GNOMES of Brussels at the risk of losing your giro cheque payments?

If you agree put a cross in the 'YES' box

If you disagree put a *firm* cross in the 'No' box.'

'What could be fairer than that, me old Robespierre?' Kev gives me an innocent stare and ze lightest mega wink yet.

On ze back of ze ballot paper is ze questionnaire on ze new Addlestone Swear-word, to replace ze out-of-date F-word. Ze selection committee 'ad a difficult job reducing ze flood of entries down to only two proposals. Many suggestions 'ad to be rejected, including funny twists like 'Cuff' and 'Drut'. But ze final selection is 'Work' and, by popular acclaim, a five-letter word has been admitted – ze most common word on TV, 'Bleep', submitted by a ten-year-old schoolgirl, Chloe Tyson, whose father is a Giro Cheque consultant.

Voting is very slow until opening time, when queues of voters line up to strike zer blow for democracy. Ze results are declared half an hour after ze pubs close. For ze referendum on Europe, ze votes cast are very few. Only 3 are cast for YES but 62 for NO. Kev 'as won by an avalanche!

'I told you, Ash mate,' Kev nudges me gently as ze result is read out, 'they'd never understand the lingo any more than those fat bastards in Parliament. They didn't notice the word '*withdrawing*', and thought YES meant voting in favour when of course it was exactly the contrary!' Ze cheers of jubilation among Rodge and 'is friends evaporate when ze returning officer angrily explains zat Addlestone 'as voted overwhelmingly to stay in Europe and ze ERM. Kev is a genius!

Next, ze F-word replacement referendum results are announced. Ze turn-out for zis vote 'as been enormous. Apparently, ze queues of voters were only interested in zis referendum, and left ze Euro voting sides blank. Ze result declared is: '"Bleep", 2,642; "WORK" 7,963'. Ze result is greeted wiz jubilation by our Giro comrades. Zey march off in glee towards ze Taxi Tavern, chanting 'Work off! Work off!' and 'He's a right Job, that John Major!'

Kev and I celebrate our Euro victory in ze 'Taxi', while Rodge and 'is chums console zemselves wiz what zey call a 'working great victory' over ze F-word. So everybody is happy. At ze end of ze evening everybody is more zan happy. Zey are 'working' and 'jobbing' at each other wiz gusto. I, too, let my hair down wiz Kev, because Absinthe is off at ze Women's Lib Institute once more wiz 'er Eiffel Tower, and probably won't be back till ze early morning hours. But I still 'ave ze comfort of my bucket, which I shall miss when Rod fits ze new roof tiles, which 'e assures me will be in 'is yard ze day after tomorrow.

Ze Taxi Tavern, following ze great British tradition, is notorious for AWOL 'usbands, as Rodge calls them, or 'usbands let out by zer wives on parole. So zer are frequent phone calls from angry wives and girlfriends in search of zer loved ones. Tonight ze bar phone rings and is answered by ze buxom barmaid, Gerry (known as 'Gerry-built', because 'er structure is deliciously wobbly), who shouts across ze bar: 'Has anyone seen Mike Hunt?' Apparently Mike is a nice councillor from ze CAB offices but, extraordinarily, all ze men in ze bar collapse into raucous guffaws, except for a few, that is, who are slightly embarrassed.

Kev is in creases, so 'elpless zat not even 'e can raise a nudge in my direction. I tell Kev I do not understand, but when 'e explains I rush straight back through ze freezing rain to Station Approach and my loving bucket. First I 'ave to take out ze flowers I put in it to celebrate our six months anniversary. I sleep tired but happy.

NOVEMBER

November 'as arrived, and ze clocks 'ave been changed to central European time. What a gesture of solidarity on ze part of ze great British people towards zer European cousins. Ze move is welcomed because it brings lighter evenings, but zer are serious objections from ze farming and flashing lobbies: farmers because zey do not like to turn on zer tractor headlights early in ze morning; flashers because zey are not visible in ze dark mornings when on early shift. Ze Runnynose Council offices are besieged by demonstrators chanting 'It's daylight robbery!' and waving banners: 'EURO-TIME'S A CRIME' carried by ze farmers and 'EURO-HOUR – ZIPPO TIME!' carried by ze flashers.

But, by a typical miracle stroke of genius, Kev diffuses ze crisis by appearing on ze entrance steps of ze CAB tower block offices to propose a brilliant compromise. Ze farmers are suggested to go to bed one hour later and get up one hour later; zat way zey can catch ze late-night porno movie. Ze farmers 'ad never thought of zat! In addition, Kev promises zem an extra EC subsidy and state assistance in raising their prices to compensate zer new unsocial hours of work. Zey are delighted, and march off in unison to check zer bank deposit accounts.

For ze flashers, Kev proposes free pencil torches from ze Council, which will allow zem to work night shifts as well! Zey, too, cheer and wave zer macs. I really think Kev should stand for Parliament.

Today is ze Sabbath once more and, according to Rodge, ze most exciting service in ze Free Range calendar: Divorcees' Sunday. 'E and all 'is divorced friends religiously make zer annual church attendance, because all ze glamorous female divorcees turn up as well. Rodge says it is much better attended zan ze Taxi Tavern's monthly 'Singles Nite', which costs five Addle Stones to enter and each drink is at least half a stone. Absinthe refuses to attend and stays in bed after another late night out at ze WLI. Before I leave, I ask 'er what she wants for 'er birthday next week. She says a retread for 'er Eiffel Tower. What a curious little blossom my 'petite poubelle' 'as become since our arrival in ze garden of Addlestone.'

Divorcees' Sunday is so popular ze animals 'ave to stay outside in ze church yard and listen to ze service over loudspeakers, which Eric Surplice 'as arranged in kind collaboration wiz ze local music shop 'Zounds!' Ze church is packed, and Rev Trev is in full fire and brimstone form. After two hymns and two hyrrhs, 'e delivers 'is most fierce attack yet on society's un-Christian rejection of single parenthood and its blind prejudice against unmarried couples.

'I ask you, brethren and sistren, were Adam and Eve ever married? Nay, verily, they were not! Are we therefore to call the whole of the human race bastards?'

A voice pipes up from ze rear pews, 'Well I haven't met any who aren't!', but Trev carries on regardless. 'And how could the human race have continued to be propagated without the pure homosexual love of Cain and Abel? The first miracle in the Bible!' Rodge gives me a nudge and whispers loud enough to be heard in ze choir stalls: 'Pushing his luck here, Ash. Why doesn't he stick to sex out of marriage and the clean stuff?'

Trev is still not perturbed and furrows on. 'I would remind you all of the scriptures of the patron saint of Addlestone, St Seth the Breath, who was martyred beneath the old crutch oak outside the Dog and Duck in 1954 for having an adulterous affair with the landlord's daughter.

Seth was cursed with halitosis all his short life, but the good Lord turned it into a blessing by forcing him to kiss ladies everywhere except on their mouths. As a result, St Seth's osculatory practices and teachings became much sought after throughout the length and breadth of Runnynose. His following of ladies, young and old, was in multitudes. There were even those who swore his pungent breath had miraculous healing properties, as long as it was employed away from the patient's mouth.

But alas, the Devil works in wondrous ways. St Seth's teachings became so popular with the female folk that many men went unto St Seth for halitosis lessons, and he reaped a harvest of pots of gold selling anchovy and garlic paste as medicine. The Devil brought down on him the jealousy of the married men, who arranged for the landlord's daughter to seduce him one night when St Seth was overflowing with the good Lord's spirit.

He breathed his heavenly fumes all over her and she was amazedly sore – sorry, brethren and sistren – she was sore amazed.

But the landlord and the Crutch Oak Vigilantes set upon St Seth as he staggered out of the inn, and clamped him into the stocks beneath the old crutch oak, where he was taunted by the locals and deprived of all liquid. He died of thirst after twenty gruelling minutes, and his spirit returned in peace to the Gutterspew distillery. Ever since then, the old crutch oak has been Addlestone's sacred monument to the saint who breathed love into the hearts of Addlestone laity.'

Rodge 'as to whisper again: 'And there's no laity like an Addlestone lay!' Another nudge sends me sliding off ze pew into ze aisle, while 'e barely suppresses 'is guffaws in ze Free Range book of 'Hyrrhs Ancient and Modern'. Trev ignores ze commotion and concludes: 'The moral of this tragic tale is: "Be like St Seth, don't hold your breath! Where love abounds get your CD's from "Zounds!"'. Rodge explains zat in order to raise funds for ze church, Trev 'as now introduced a message from a weekly sponsor at ze end of every sermon. Trev rounds off ze show wiz a stirring guitar accompaniment to 'These Boots Were Made for Walking' and 'Hate is a Many-Splendoured Thing'. 'E delivers ze blessing: 'Whom God Hath Put Asunder Let No Man Join Together.'

Trev and 'is backing choir 'ave 'ardly reached ze exit before ze congregation breaks pews, and ze worshippers scramble for ze objects of zer desire, clambering over ze pews and scattering prayer books in zer wake.

'I'm not letting Rod get to that blonde over there in the pink leggings first.' Rodge blurts out as 'e hurdles over six pews to a rather elegant lady who is trying to extricate 'erself from ze religious fervour of Les ze Lech, as 'e blocks 'er exit into ze aisle wiz 'is walking stick. I decide it is unseemly to engage in such sport in zis holy place, despite Trev ze Rev's encouragement, and beat a discreet retreat to ze Dog and Duck to start on my Sunday Spews.

Ten minutes later Rodge shows up, downcast and in dire need of a copious injection of Super Spew Extra. 'e explains ze blonde is a 'airdresser wiz a rich sugar daddy in Rotweiler country, who only came over for ze service to check out ze female competition. Rodge is tee'd off.

'What chance have I got against the Clitterati of St George's Hills? Women like that shouldn't be allowed in on Divorcees' Sunday if they don't have dishonourable intentions. 'Course I blame that Trev the Rev. Doesn't know his seraphim from his cherubim when it comes to normal sex. All that stuff about Cain and Abel and Seth the Breath. Trev's the one with halitosis – at the wrong end!' And wiz zat Rodge demonstrates vociferously zat 'e is no mean contender in zat department, himself.

Finally, at closing time, just before four o'clock, Absinthe arrives from 'er slumbers for an after-hours Babycham, which is never a problem at ze Dog and Duck. She persuades me to go to ze new super take-away which 'as just opened in ze High Street, and offers to pay for both of us wiz Stones she 'as earned during 'er late-night charity work at ze Women's Lib Institute.

We meander down ze High Street to ze new 'Super-Naff Caff'. Scrawled on its walls and windows is an impressive range of services to cater for every possible taste: 'Breakfast 24 hours a day – lunches – High Teas – Low Teas – A La Carte Dinners – Candlelight Elevenses – Champagne Cocktails – Snacks – Frozen Toasties – OAP Soup Kitchen – Free Deliveries – Rooms to Let by the Hour – Ear-Piercing While U Wait – Take-away Book-keeping.'

How enterprising ze English are, especially ze Super-Naff Caff owner Mr Singh! Absinthe and I opt for a take-away candlelight supper. Unfortunately, ze candles blow out before we get back to Station Approach, but we manage to relight zem and enjoy our frozen custard curry toasties washed down wiz a glorious glass of Cornish Pastis, topped up wiz Addlestone Sewage Works recycled ice cubes.

In order to replenish ze Council's overstretched Giro Cheque coffers, Kev 'as come up wiz yet another brilliant brainwave: to privatize yellow-line marking.

'You see, my old matelot,' he explains, 'many of the old yellow lines have lost their original glossy bloom, and in any case, all the single lines should probably be made double now. In fact, I'm proposing we should abolish single yellow lines altogether and and introduce triple, and even quadruple, lines, to indicate the gravity of the fine that will be imposed if violated. Of course, there aren't many streets left without yellow lines in Addlestone, but I reckon a really keen privatized outfit would be very creative and find lots of new opportunities, don't you reckon, Ash?'

I nod agreement, but inwardly my heart sinks at ze thought of our beautiful village being desecrated by ze racist anti-parking fanatics. 'And another great idea, mon ashtray,' Kev goes on, 'we're going to make them use fluorescent paint so that the lines shine in the dark!' Kev leans close. 'Don't tell a soul, but I've patented the idea because it'll make all the roadsides visible in the dark – the greatest advance in road safety since the invention of the cats-eyes. Could catch on nationally with any luck, don't you think? Then I could retire to that camp-site in Provence! Anyway, Runnynose Council benefits two ways: one by selling the concession to the highest bidder; two by selling off shares to the public. Should keep the Giro Cheques going for another month or two!' Kev gives ze mega-wink and reaches for 'is new foaming pint of Spew.

Kev lurches off to ze Council meeting where 'is proposals are voted for unanimously, and Cliff Roakes' nephew is immediately awarded ze yellow line contract under ze company name Jaundiced Enterprises, whose slogan, devised by Wally Connall, is 'Triple Yellow Lines Mean Triple Fines!' For a breath of fresh air I go over to ze 'Brewer's Droop' to say hello to Marie Celeste, whose blouse I 'ave not looked down for at least forty-eight hours.

'Long time no see, Monsieur Mange-Minge,' Marie greets me wiz a naughty leer and reaches down for a bottle of Veuve Twankey from ze fridge, revealing all 'er voluptuous loveliness. I am on my second bottle when suddenly through ze door bursts Nigel Fortescue-Weathercock Bart, resplendent in pink mambo-dot cravat, brass-buttoned navy blazer and white slacks wiz Reebok trainers to match, and full of 'joie de vivre'.

'Hiya, my old French bean! How's life?' 'E greets me as Marie bends down for a bottle of 'is special bubbly from ze fridge.

'No female company today, Mr Bart?' I venture.

'A little bit later, old Mange-Tout. She doesn't finish at the Pol Pot till three. A touch of the orientals this time. Cute little morceau. She certainly knows how to serve Peking Duck.' Nige gives me a refined aristocratic wink and takes another swig from ze neck of 'is favourite 'shampoo', Tête et Epaules Anti-Pelliculaire Spumante.

'Her name's Chu Mai Kok. I call her "Slitty", because of her eyes of course. Quite tiny. Have to carry a shoe horn in my back pocket, ha ha ha!' Nige swigs another slurp of shampoo.

I tell Nige I cannot wait to witness zis momentous tryst, but 'e insists on telling me about ze St Hillians' fox hunt next Saturday. 'E is sure I am a brilliant horseman because I come from near ze Camargue, and he invites me to join ze hunt next weekend. I do not like to tell 'im I 'ave only ridden donkeys along ze bottom-less beach at St Tropez, when my father 'ad ze donkey ride concession – which was less for riding zan hiring out to couples late at night.

Reluctanly, I agree to take part, but Nige 'as to explain me ze rules, which 'e does after another bottle of Anti-Pelliculaire. It seems strange to me zat when ze object is to kill ze fox ze 'unt 'as to chase it for kilometres and kilometres at great risk first, when in France we would shoot on sight. Ze English call it sport: to me it is inefficiency. We agree to meet next Saturday morning at ze St Hillians' lodge, where Nige will provide me wiz 'is uncle's 'hunting pink', a docile horse and a large glass of sherry to take ze chill off ze November frost. What 'ave I let myself in for? But I understand it is all in a good cause because ze foxes are vermin and must be exterminated.

I bid Nige 'au revoir' till Saturday, and decide to pick up a Pol Pot take-away and sample zer new Chinese dish – but she has already left.

Next morning, Absinthe is not too tired to bring me breakfast in bed: our usual favourite English diet of stewed prunes, Brilo-Bran, scrambled eggs and free-range beans, washed down wiz stewed tea sweetened by saccharine wiz no added sugar. Absinthe 'as put ze *Addlestone Strumpet* on ze tray. It carries a momentous front-page headline: 'Sick English Children Airlifted to Bosnia'. Apparently Nadir Tours 'ave arranged flights to Sarajevo for English cases who 'ave been waiting hope-lessly for hospital beds on ze NHS, so zat zey can join ze queues in Bosnia and get priority treatment back in ze UK! One child was refused treatment by 'er local UK hospital because 'er parents were smokers, but when she arrived in Sarajevo she was put at ze top of ze list and flown to a UK hospital straight away. 'Ow charitable ze English are to people from abroad!

Two days later we are awakened by ze noise of workmen out-side ze front of ze cottage. Immediately I think it must be Rod wiz our roof tiles, and go down to ze cellar to carry up a crate of cool Gutterspew. But I am mistaken. Kev's privatization of ze yellow lines 'as got off to a flying start. A team of workmen, I spot through ze net curtains, are piling shovels and paint canisters into a yellow van, which I think carries ze logo 'Jaundiced Enterprises'. I bolt down my stewed prunes and Brillo-Bran and take ze consequences in record time, finding a dual purpose for our new Turkish loo, which provides me wiz a simultaneous shower. I race out in my silk dressing-gown to discover what is 'appening.

As I open ze front door, I am just in time to see ze Jaundiced van disappearing round ze end of Station Approach. To my 'orror, ze yellow peril 'as struck. Not only 'ave zey painted triple yellow lines all along Station Approach, but zey 'ave even put double yellow lines all around our front yard and all ze way up our front door steps, and given our wheely-bin a ticket. Even parked cars in ze street 'ave triple yellow lines painted along their bodywork because zey did not move away in time before ze deadly line-marking machine passed by, marking everything in its path.

I get dressed in Foreign Legion fatigues, specially designed by Yves Cardin, and march angrily up to ze Runnynose Council offices in furious protest. Ze yellow lines are everywhere. It is like a 'orror movie. Even Safeways 'as double yellow lines round ze Zimmerframe park, where a Pay and Display machine 'as been erected. In ze Runnynose offices ze yellow lines are along every corridor and up every staircase. Apparently, ze concept 'as been extended from no parking for cars to no waiting for pedestrians. Traffic wardens are on every corner, lurking in every corridor, pouncing on innocent Zimmerframes and loitering pedestrians wiz exhorbitant tickets. I burst into Kev's luxury suite, and demand an explanation for this tyranny. 'E ushers me into a seat, calls for coffee from 'is personal assistant, ze buxom 'Gerry-Built', and tries to calm my nerves.

'Be reasonable, mon cher Euro-frog. We need the money. Addlestone is mega-skint unless we can raise public cash. This is the only way. This cosmic initiative of mine will be financially supported by our noble friends in Brussels to the tune of two million quid, or ten million Addle Stones! Tell me honestly, Ash mate, do you honestly believe we can keep our Giro mountain without injections of cash? And look on the bright side: tourists from all over the country will come pouring in to see the yellow lines shining in the night! We'll be building holiday caravan sites like they're going out of style to cope with the influx!'

My heart sinks again. They're going to destroy my darling little village. 'But, Kev, I still haven't had *my* Giro Cheque,' I moan.

'That's all solved, Ashy boy,' Kev winks, getting out of 'is Parker Knoll executive swivel chair. 'Let's hop out and I'll explain to you over a pint.'

We pick our way through ze teams of marauding traffic wardens, resplendent in zer new reflective yellow uniforms. In ze Taxi Tavern, I am surprised to see Gerry behind ze bar after just making an appearance as Kev's secretary. Kev explains she 'as several fully paid part-time jobs because she is such an obliging worker – she and Kev exchange glances – except, zat is, when she's not taking time off to claim benefit. Kev and Gerry enjoy ze joke. In any case, she only works behind ze bar during opening hours, when Kev is usually out of ze office anyway.

'Here's how you get your Giro, Ash,' Kev begins after 'is first pint of Gutterspew Winter Willy-Warmer. 'The difficulty you've 'ad is being a Frogman. We give benefits galore to duskies from the far corners of our once-great empire, and we're particularly generous towards pale-skins who come from former Communist countries that have opted for democracy, famine and civil war. But Frogs, Degoes, Krouts, Eyeties and Scans, no chance! So what we're going to do, my old Frog leg, is change your name – don't get worried, only slightly, and only for benefit purposes – to 'Ashley Peabody'. Just like I did for the election, remember? It's easy peasy, I'll show you how at the Deed Poll office. 'Course it'll cost you a few Winter Willy-Warmers!' Kev slams 'is empty glass down on ze counter and beams expectantly.

'Kev, I 'ave to say once again: you are a genius! You'd make a great Prime Minister, you know.'

Kev spits on ze floor. 'No chance, Froggie. I don't want to be an Avon lady – all cosmetics and make-up, window-dressing and cover-up, fur coat and no knickers. No thanks. I couldn't afford the RADA lessons. And in any case, I'd refuse the operation to get the voice right! On the other hand, the Swiss bank account could be tolerated without too much grief. No, Ash, I'm better off as a big prick in a small brothel. Another Spew?'

After a couple more, I go to ze local tyre depot to get an estimate for retreading ze Eiffel Tower, since Absinthe's 'eart seems to be set on it for 'er birthday. I am still undecided which

114

take-away to treat 'er to on ze magic night, which also happens to be our twentieth wedding anniversary. I am looking forward to it, because Absinthe 'as promised me I can dispense wiz my beloved bucket if I retread ze Eiffel Tower in time. I'm not sure what she means, but I pretend it is an offer I can't refuse.

On ze way back to Station Approach, I bump into ze Brain as 'e is being poured out of ze Dog and Duck, which 'as very thoughtfully introduced a brilliant new system to 'elp session drinkers 'ome wizout ze expense of taxi fares: it is called 'ZimmerRent'. For ze price of a pint, Bruiser Reade's voluptuous daughter Sharon will rent you a frame and provide a tag wiz your name, address and phone number in case of transit problems. Ze service is available 24 hours a day, wiz a front lamp and rear reflectors for night use.

I intercept ze Brain pushing his frame ze wrong way home, and turn 'im round in ze right direction. Through coughing spluts, which never seem to dislodge 'is cigarette, 'e apologizes for disturbing me, but explains zat ze long-awaited Eurovision Karaoke Song Contest 'as finally been fixed for December. Ze problem, apparently, 'as not been ze Eurovision TV link-ups or ze international presenters in each country, but ze reservation at ze Addlestone First Brownie Pack Nissen Hut Hall, which 'as been booked solid for months wiz important local events like ze Women's Lib Institute's 'Boadicea Karate Course', ze Addlestone Film Society's Jeremy Beadle Video Rejects Season, and ze Addlestone Open University Tattoo-ology life classes – very popular among lady students, who queue up to see Professor Mick Ange pose for zem to create zer own designs on 'is 'unky frame. I promise ze Brain to attend ze next Karaoke planning meeting wiz Wally Connall and Kev to finalize sponsorship arrangements and accommodation plans for ze visiting foreign contestants.

Next evening, I attend ze Karaoke Song Contest meeting in ze Dog and Duck snug, and we fix ze dates and all ze details. Individual caravans will be arranged for ze television presenters, and shared mobile-home rooms for ze star singers. It is agreed zat, although it is titled ze '*Eurovision* Karaoke Song Contest', we should open Europe's frontiers to ze developing world. We vote overwhelmingly to include entrants from ze Golan Heights, Albania, ze ex-Soviet Union, Hong Kong and even Bangladesh (because one entrant is now running a take-away in Southall).

'Ow democratic and globally minded ze British are! Wally Connall agrees to bring 'is hi-fi equipment to ze Nissen Hut next week so zat Sharon, from ze Dog and Duck, and I can rehearse our presentation of ze songs.

After ze meeting, we adjourn for further deliberations in ze Coq. Wally is boasting about 'is new estate car, which 'e 'as just bought to replace 'is old Volvo. 'E tells us it 'as been specially built to protect wives and children from ze dangers of Addlestone traffic. 'E drags us into ze car park to show off 'is magnificent new limousine.

'It comes with a revolutionary wife-proof insurance policy, with instructions on how to cope in the very unlikely event of an accident'. Wally insists we all read ze accident instructions:

THE VOLVO GUIDE TO SURVIVING AN ACCIDENT

IN THE UNLIKELY EVENT YOU ARE INVOLVED IN AN ACCIDENT IN YOUR ACCIDENT-PROOF VOLVO WE ADVISE YOUR STUPID WIFE (FOR WHOM YOU BOUGHT THIS TANK IN THE FIRST PLACE) TO FOLLOW THESE PROCEDURES:-

(A) IN EXTREME CASES WHERE YOUR VOLVO UNBE-LIEVABLY KNOCKS OVER A PEDESTRIAN:

(i) Turn off the engine and get out of the car: check that there are no scratches or bloodstains on your vehicle; if any, immediately use your mobile phone to contact your insurance company;
(ii) Phone your family to check your children are safely home and the stove is not burning the dinner; check that you are not missing your favourite TV programmes;
(iii) Phone your mother/uncle/boyfriend not to panic if anything appears on the local TV news;
(iv) Check the victim on the tarmac for any twitches; DO NOT attempt mouth-to-mouth resuscitation unless you have a condom in your handbag;
(v) In case of remaining twitches DO NOT use your own mobile phone (it is too expensive); ask a passer-by to phone for an ambulance;
(vi) If no remaining twitches or response to pumelling, DO NOT use your mobile phone; ask a passer-by to dial 999 for the

police; this should give you at least half-an-hour to call your lawyer or drive off for a Singapore Sling in the comfort of your own home before the police arrive.

(B) IN CASE OF MINOR ACCIDENTS: complain to the Advertising Standards Authority.

REMEMBER: YOU ARE NEVER GUILTY IN A VOLVO, unless you drive through a first-floor plate glass window without an Equity card!

Please be kind enough to ask the little woman to complete the following brief questionnaire, which will help your friendly VOLVO dealer improve his service to you and your family:-

HOW DID YOU FIRST HEAR ABOUT OUR NEW VOL-VO SUPER-INJECTION VIBRO-TURBO?

From TV advertising?

From your local friendly dealer?

From reading the drunk-driving reports in the local press?

Please hand this questionnaire in to your friendly local dealer: BANGERS 'N' SMASH: Gasworks Crescent, Addlestone.

Thank you.
BJÖRN JESTERDAY, Chairman.

Back in ze bar we all 'ooh' and 'aah' about Wally's new acquisition. Rodge ze Dodge 'as just come in through ze car park.

'Not bad for a Scan-mobile, Wally. Have you tried the injector seat yet?' Rodge winks in all directions. Wally puffs up and declares: 'You don't need an ejector seat in a Volvo: it is proof against all aggressions from other motorists.'

'Not *ejector* seat, Wally,' Rodge nearly loses a mouthful of Gutterspew in his mirth, '*in*jector seat for your travelling companions. Don't tell me Vulva technicians haven't got beyond the central locking and personal vibrator seats yet?' Rodge's remarks are considered in bad taste, but not enough to refuse the glasses of Spew Extra Export he offers us.

Back at Five Station Approach, I wait for Absinthe's return from ze WLI in front of ze new privatized TV channel which has just started on air from ze St George's Hills transmitter. It is called Craven TV Channel A, a very clever move by ze sponsor, because cigarette advertising is banned but no one can stop zem using zer call sign 'Craven A' twenty-five times an hour. It is a very progressive yet socially caring and user-friendly station.

Zey 'ave a sophisticated system of watersheds, which I discover are not ze local met office's. Ze cut-off time for under fives is 2 pm; for ten-year-olds, grannies and grandads it is 5pm, after which ze adult programmes begin and last up to 7.30, when it is every man for 'imself and wall-to-wall video nasties.

But ze most novel innovation of all is ze presentation of ze national and international news: it is run as a game show under ze exciting title '*You Choose The News*!' Disaster scenes from all over ze world are projected on to a big multi-screen and individual contestants 'ave to guess which one will be selected by ze viewers who phone in ze choice, which is zen shown in a full news report; ze contestant wins £5,000 if 'e/she 'as chosen ze same item as ze viewers. After 'world disasters' ze next section is 'sex scandals', where famous personalities are projected on ze big screen and another vote is cast. Ze next section is 'cuddly pet corner', followed by ze joke department, where viewers 'ave to select a scene from the House of Commons – invariably ze Prime Minister wins ze vote. Ze English 'ave such a sense of humour, even ze politicians are professional comedians!

Ze day of ze St Hillians' hunt arrives, and I drive over through ze early morning mist to ze Lodge, fortified wiz a hip-flask of Cornish Pastis to calm ze moths in my stomach. Nige ushers me to ze changing rooms, where 'e 'as kindly prepared my kit. Ze pink jacket is two sizes too large and ze jodhpurs are two sizes too small: I think I shall 'ave a problem climbing astride ze 'orse.

Outside, I am introduced to ze meet and my 'orse, Rodeo Romeo, who is terrifyingly enormous and snorts every few seconds. Embarrassingly, after ten unsuccessful attempts, I 'ave to be 'elped on to Romeo's back. I 'ave barely got 'old of ze reins when ze general order to mount is given, at which, to my 'orror, my super stallion takes ze signal to mount a nearby mare 'e 'as taken a fancy to. I am powerless to restrain 'im, and 'ave to 'ang on wiz my arms round 'is neck to avoid being thrown off by ze bucking movements. Ze other riders 'owl wiz refined laughter while I turn as pink as my jacket.

When Romeo 'as finished, Nige consoles me. 'Well at least you know how to hang on now over the fences! Come over and meet my papa.'

Unfortunately, I cannot get Romeo to budge, so Nige's papa 'as to come over to meet me. Nige introduces Lord Singein'

Doberman, who is sporting a bushy drop-handlebar moustache and a monocle. When I look round I notice I am ze only one not wearing a monocle!

'Pleased to meet you, Monsieur Blanche-Tout. I've always been a great believer in the Entente Cordial. Talking of which, can we all 'ave another stirrup cup, Scrote?' Ze wrinkled retainer scurries off to ze bar to bring out more fortifiers for ze terrible ordeal to come.

'Hope you like our "strop cup", as we call it, Blanche-Tout,' Doberman continues. 'It's a traditional St Hillian cocktail, made of frozen prune juice, chilled Irish coffee, powdered cenapods and a large squirt of whipped evaporated milk. The most delicious long drink pick-me-up in the empire!'

I am puzzled. 'But I thought, your Lordliness, zat cocktails could only be short drinks. When I was wiz my cousin once in a famous cocktail bar in Milan, I read an article in ze Corriere della Sera by an English expert no less, who explained zat ze origin of ze word cocktail comes from ze fox-hunting 'orses in ze nineteenth century, which wore docked tails in ze shape of cock's tails because zey were not thoroughbred, so ze drinks ze hunting set swigged were called cocktails because zey were alcohol diluted wiz a little juice, zat is, not thoroughbred spirit.'

I sit back in my saddle, proud of my dissertation. An embarrassing silence falls on ze monocled meet and I realize I have made a mistake trying to teach ze aristocracy zer own history. I am afraid zey may not 'elp me on to a 'orse ever again. I will never understand ze English. What a farce to chase dangerously over 'ill and dale to catch an animal zat 'as already been caught and 'as to be released in order to be caught all over again!

'Owever, I am sure zat my liaison wiz ze aristocracy will be rewarding. After two more strop cups, and a secret swig from my hip flask, I am semi-prepared for ze off. Suddenly, ze fox is released, and after a minute or so ze hounds are let go. What wonderful British fair play to give ze fox such a start before killing it! If only ze Spanish could be so kind to zer bulls.

Lord Doberman smashes 'is strop cup to ze ground and lets out an enormous tiger roar from 'is saddle region and everybody is off, shouting 'tally-ho!' Everybody, zat is, except Romeo and me, who stay rooted to ze spot until Romeo spots 'is favourite mare galloping across ze fields, at which 'e rears up, snorts from both ends and takes off at a lightning gallop wiz me 'anging on to 'is mane for dear life.

Ze hunt is now quite a long way ahead, but Romeo is determined to catch ze grey mare. No amount of tugging on ze reins 'olds back 'is enthusiasm. I am in agony from saddle battery and excruciating jodhpurs, until at ze first fence Romeo mercifully throws me into a ditch. I am saddle-sore and bleeding from ze brambles, and furious at zis barbarous British sport. I take a swig from my 'ip-flask, undo my jodhpur flies to give me room to walk, and stomp back across ze fields to ze St Hillians Lodge in high dungeon. Back in ze Lodge bar, Scrote sneeringly offers me a consolatory strop cup. I am fuming to 'ave been so humiliated by ze British aristocracy, and resolve to take my revenge to uphold ze honour of my fatherland. I storm off to my Volvo, drive back to Station Approach to get my Four Ten double-barrelled shotgun. If 'ey want to kill ze fox I will show zem ze efficient way, French style and no messing!

Despite British fair play in allowing zer quarry to run ze foxglove, zey know exactly which route ze fox will take to get to its earth so, after loading my gun, I drive off to lie in wait at Brooklands Corner by ze entrance to Tesco's new giant megamarket. I do not 'ave to wait long. Ze sound of baying hounds approaches, and in ze distance I see ze grey mare galloping along wiz Romeo on 'er back.

Suddenly, ze fox appears, loping through ze wheely-bins into ze car park, exhausted and gasping from ze chase. I think it is a far far better thing I do now to put ze creature out of its misery. My first shot just wounds it but my second finishes 'im off brilliantly. I come out from behind ze bottle bank and sprint across ze car park to claim my prize before ze hounds destroy my well-earned meal. Unfortunately, ze hounds get zer first and leave very little for my supper. But zen ze 'untsmen arrive and scream at me because I 'ave cheated them of zer prey. Lord Doberman is particularly angry.

'Absolute disgrace! Absolute disgrace! Killing a defenceless animal in cold blood. Should never have let a Frog-Wallah in. Common Market'll be the death of us. Get the police, put him in irons!'

I cannot believe my ears, but I am immediately seized by ze riders, who descend from zer 'orses and strap me to ze ground. A police car is called for me and an RSPCA ambulance for ze eviscerated fox. Ze ambulance arrives in three minutes but ze police take an hour, by which time my arms are numb. At ze police station in Addlestone I am refused access to a phone and a lawyer, on ze grounds I 'ave violated animal rights and do not qualify for 'uman treatment. I am worried about phoning Absinthe but it is one of 'er Women's Lib Institute evenings so zer is no point.

Eventually, at midnight, after closing time, I am allowed a phone call to Kev, who comes and bails me out for a crate of Gutterspew, to be 'eld by ze Police Benevolent Fund. Kev takes me back to Station Approach where we drown our sorrows in Cornish Pastis washed down wiz copious mounts of Spew Extra. I am very upset about British justice, but Kev explains me ze system.

'Don't take it to heart, my old Ashtray. The Brits invented right and wrong long before you lot crawled out of your frogspawn. We don't have a constitution but that's deliberate. It means our legal system is very flexible. Can't be dominated by any one class, except the lawyers of course. It's best to have no rules, 'cos that way the legals can make them up as they go along. So, in your case, my French cinders, a legal prince charming friend of mine will get you off with no sweat. All you'll need to do is fill his glass slipper with Giro Cheques marinated in champagne!'

At which point Kev slumps asleep on ze Louis Quatorze divan, megasnoring, and I clamber upstairs to give my bucket a goodnight hug. I am nervous about ze trial, which is set for December 10th, but I trust Kev complicitly.

But now it is Absinthe's birthday. I cannot exactly remember 'ow old she is, but I do know we first went together on ze beach at St Tropez when she 'ad graced only fifteen summers and I was but a callow youth of twelve. At breakfast I present 'er wiz 'er retreaded Eiffel Tower. Before she races upstairs wiz it, manage to explain to 'er zat I am taking 'er out to ze new Afro-Arab restaurant zat 'as just opened in ze High Street, ze 'King Solomon's Mines'.

Ze restaurant doesn't serve alcohol, so Absinthe and I sneak in two hipflasks of Babycham. Ze meal is exquisite: Salam Salami as starter, two Ladies' Fingers (as a concession to Western feminism), Donor Kebab (fresh from ze hospital) wiz Solomon Rusty Chips, followed by raw pig's liver, which Absinthe refuses because of ze transplant shortage, all washed down by a giant 'Gobsmacker' – ginger ale, orange and bitter lemon, which goes down very well wiz a topping of Babycham.

As a special surprise treat, I 'ave arranged for ze owner to bring in a cake in ze shape of Absinthe's favourite symbol, ze Eiffel Tower, wiz just one candle on top because I cannot remember how old she is, and in any case I do not think she can manage a serious blow-job after all zese years. We toast each other in Gobsmackers and zen race to ze Dog and Duck for a serious nightcap.

After midnight we share a Zimmerframe 'Taxi' back to Station Approach and, wearing dark glasses, take a blinder of Cornish Pastis watching ze late news on 'Craven A' TV. It is ze usual menu of massacre, rape and sex scandals until ze commercial break, when a wonderful new product is advertised by Her Maj, 'Anus Horribilis,' ze latest haemorrhoid cure, wiz ze slogan 'The horse trials of the Royals prove we have no piles or boils!'

As a special concession to Absinthe's glorious birthday, she allows me to sleep wiz 'er Eiffel Tower, and in return I let 'er 'ave my bucket. I set ze alarm early because Rod is coming round wiz ze roof tiles tomorrow morning – I think!

DECEMBER

Z e British winter 'as arrived again – so soon! Ze whore frost is on our back lawn, and soon ze little birds will be flying in for scraps of stale sliced loaf crusts and Brillo-Bran packet ends so zat I can shoot zem for our starling and sparrow pie Sunday lunch.

Not surprisingly, Rod and 'is team do not show up wiz ze roof tiles but, just as we are finishing our stewed prunes and cenapod omelettes, ze phone rings. It is Rod to say 'e cannot come until ze frost clears because it will be too slippery on ze roof, so we must be patient for a day or two. Absinthe and I resign ourselves to our fate and drown our sorrows in orange juice and pastis, our special breakfast cocktail, which we 'ave named 'Addlestone Sunrise'.

But I am glad there will be no distraction from Rod and 'is merry men, because today it is my trial for ze murder of ze fox. My solicitor. Robin Greenwood, 'as told me to dress in my Divorcees' Sunday best, so I wear my Dijon mustard Pierre Laurent suit wiz pink Valentino shirt, psychedelic TV news-announcer tie, Gucci trainers and Marks and Spencer 100 per cent acrylic socks.

Absinthe drives me to ze court house and parks next to Robin's Ferrari. 'E asks me to remain cool because ze Animal Rights Protection International Tigers (ARMPIT) are going to be in ze public gallery together wiz ze RSPCA, which is collaborating wiz ze St Hillians to accuse me of cruelty to animals. But I have one ally, Mayor Cliff Roakes' sister, Twiggie, from ze garden centre, who 'as turned up because she objects to ze hunt destroying all ze grass and fences: she believes passionately zat plants need protection more zan animals since zey cannot speak or run away, and she is a founder-member of ze Committee for Rapid Action to Protect Plants. I thank 'er for showing up in support, but Robin thinks we 'ave little chance, especially since ze *Addlestone Strumpet* is present, which means maximum publicity, so ze magistrates will not be lenient.

I want to plead 'not guilty', but Robin 'as persuaded me zer is no chance, because I cannot deny ze act, and so I plead 'guilty wiz extenuating circumstances'. Before we are called into ze court room, I take a final swig from my Cornish Pastis hip-flask in ze Gents' toilet and pause to admire ze legal grafitti. 'Group 4 transport and privatized jails guaranteed – phone Robin Greenwood on 0932 564393': 'If you must tell the truth be economical, it saves legal fees – Bobby Armstrong'. I am disturbed in my reverie by Robin who calls me into ze court.

In ze public gallery are all my opponents angrily waving banners: 'The Day of the French Jackal', 'Hands Off Our Foxes' and 'Fox You, Froggie!'. I am mortified. Ze prosecution reads out ze charges: I am accused of fox molesting, animal cruelty, besticide, bad sportsmanship, disturbing ze peace of ze St Hillians' hunt and inciting my 'orse to obscene acts in public. Ze key witness is of course Lord Doberman himself who, puce wiz fury and orally frothing, accuses me of single-handedly importing French farmers' and fishermen's tactics into ze noble sport of British fox-hunting. Ze gallery applaudes 'is every statement and whistles at my name so zat ze clerk of ze court 'as to call many times for silence.

But Robin Greenwood is not easily beaten. 'E pleads diminished responsibility on ze grounds I am still emotionally deprived of shooting everything on four legs and two wings in France, and 'ave not yet adjusted to civlized British hunting rules and regulations. My doctor kindly testifies zat I am suffering from withdrawal symptoms, and I personally testify I 'onestly believed I was saving ze fox from a cruel death by putting it out of its misery. Fortunately, none of my neighbours are present to point out how many starlings and sparrows I shot from ze spare bedroom window last January!

Finally, ze bench retires and, after what seems like a decade, returns wiz ze verdict. I am acquitted on all charges on ze grounds of permanent insanity because I am French. However, because of ze 'orse obscenity charge, I must attend a special animal therapy course at ze local privatized mental health clinic, to learn to control animals' sexual urges. Unfortunately, my goldfish, Napoleon, will be on probation to attend ze course wiz me to prove we are sexually compatible. But Robin winks at me to indicate zis is a very good solution. What a victory for British justice! Ze animal rights people in ze gallery explode into boos and hisses but Twiggie, Absinthe and Marie Celeste, who I did not know would turn up to give me immoral support, all clap and cheer and I walk out a free man! We all adjourn to ze Coq au Vin to crack a bottle of Château Anti-Pelliculaire.

Kev, Rodge, Rod and Wally are all zer to share my victory and Château Shampoo, which I do quite willingly for once. Everybody toasts my victory over ze St Hillians, and Robin explains I will only 'ave to attend ze clinic a few times wiz my beloved Napoleon before getting a clean bill of health. I say nothing about my bucket and Absinthe's reconditioned Eiffel Tower. But Rodge disagrees wiz Robin very strongly.

'Not so sure, my old frogspawn! Once you're in the system they've got you by the frizzy bits and never let go unless you play it deepfrozen. Just be careful, Ash, once their claws are in. An ex-mate of mine, Maurice Goodhill, quite a gent once, from the other side of the border on St George's Molehills, got done for driving over the limit, and was thrown out of the local "dry cleaning" clinic for turning up drunk! What sort of therapy's that, I ask you? Lost his Klaptomania import/export matchbox business – went bust! Just chill it real cool, my old Ash tray, or they mightn't let you and Napoleon out.' Rodge turns to ze bar for another bottle of 'Euro-Fizz', as 'e calls it. I feel immoralized once again.

'Don't listen to that horse manure, Monsieur Mange-N'Importe-Quoi!' an aristocratic voice pipes up from ze doorway wiz a delicious fresh Peking duck on 'is arm. I am not at all delighted to see Nigel Weathercock Bart so soon after my trial. 'Sorry about my papa, me old haricot. Didn't want to hurt you meself, but had to keep a low profile. Got me allowance to think of, you know. Let me buy you a Twankey and introduce the love of my life, Chu Mai Kok.'

Ze others turn zer, backs and I decline 'is offer as gracefully as I can, leaving 'im and 'is sleek 'Suzie Wong' to enjoy neck-swigging zer shampoo before making a vertical move up ze back stairs prior to a ninety degree change of direction.

Marie Celeste slips me another bottle 'sur la maison' wiz an inviting low bosom courtesy so I bid Absinthe and Twiggie an exciting evening at ze WLI, 'oping my beloved 'as not forgotten 'er Eiffel Tower, and return to ze bar and Marie Celeste.

Unfortunately, my romantic mood is somewhat interrupted by my Addlestonian colleagues, who are by now in 'igh spumante spirits. 'The trouble with the world today,' Rodge's speech begins, 'is that nobody understands a blind thing any more, because nobody knows what direction they're going in.

For twenty years the trade unions and the socialists did everything to destroy capitalism. The final touch came when the greatest socialist since Karl Marx, namely Maggie Thatcher, finished the job by selling off for cash the only assets the country had left, thus bankrupting the economy and bringing on the biggest recession since the Black Death. And now we can't even afford to pay for all the benefits and Giro Cheques required by our glorious socialist state. There's nothing more to sell off except the Royal Family and Margaret Thatcher's memoires.'

Thankfully, Rodge is interrupted by Nige Bart who stumbles down ze stairs and orders another Veuve Twankey, which 'e proceeds to slurp from ze neck on 'is way back up to 'is young friend. But Rodge is unstoppable and ze rest of us 'ave to drown our indifference in ze usual way.

He carries on, 'And what happens during the West's self-destruction of capitalism?' Rodge takes another swig. 'The Eastern Bloc starts dismantling communism in favour of the glories of capitalism! With resultant chaos, rampant inflation and civil war, which the Americans glorify as democracy!' Rodge takes a welcome break in ze Gents while Kev orders another swift bottle 'on important council business'.

Rod says it is difficult to stop Rodge in full flood, to which Kev suggests 'e keeps 'is flood for ze Gents. But it is not to be. 'E returns even more flooded.

'The only people who've got the right answer are the Chinese: a capitalist country with socialist venerials. No pseudo-democracy or food queues or Bosnification for them: just the fastest-growing economy in the world. They must be doing something right!' With which 'e storms out in search of 'a pint of real Gutterspew', cursing ze 'Euro-Fizz' shampoo I 'ave been buying 'im all evening.

Kev shakes 'is 'ead in dismay. 'Our local little "Pontifax Maximus"! Talking through his "ex cathedra" again. I apologize, Ash, for "mon ami sauvage". Some haven't had the benefit of an Addlestone Open University education like us lot. He's not all bad but his mouth's too big for his brains sometimes.'

Kev zen explains over our umpteenth blinder zat out poet friend Andronicus – Winston Thatcher to 'is literary public – is 'olding a new poetry festival evening next week to coincide wiz ze Eurovision Karaoke Song Contest. Unfortunately, 'e tells me, ze Karaoke Song Contest 'as 'ad to be modified to a EuroRodio Contest because of lack of funds from international sponsors, but I am still invited to be compère wiz ze beautiful Sharon from ze Dog and Duck. I hope Marie Celeste will not be too jealous.

Next morning, Absinthe kindly wakes me wiz a well-judged bowl of cenaped flakes and orange juice, laced wiz Cornish Pastis to combat ze grandmother of all hangovers, but it does no good. Ze postman 'as brought us a letter from our bank, Great Britain Holdings, which reads like hogswill, but in my current state so would anything. I decide to ask Rodge, our one-time accountant, to decipher it for me but on second thoughts I decide it is safer to show it to Wally Connall, who I must meet about ze Karaoke Contest sponsorship.

We meet in ze Dog and Duck so Wally and I can keep Sharon abreast of what's happening. She is looking particularly delicious zis morning, although of course hangovers always raise my hormone level. Neverzeless, I am most impressed by 'er white suit wiz navy blue trim and 'er hair held up in a 'igh pony-tail by a bright scarlet 'scrunchie' as she calls it.

'You didn't 'ave to dress up for me, my fellow compère!' I try to joke.

'Why, would you prefer me without the suit, then?' Sharon gives me 'er up-from-undies look, causing Wally to spill 'is pint. I try to recover my composure by gulping down my much-needed Spew Extra Export.

'I 'ope you won't say anything like zat on ze Karaoke night, mamzelle,' I plead.

'Well, the listeners won't be able to see whether I'm wearing anything or not, will they?' Sharon purrs, leaning very low across ze bar, forcing me to break for ze toilet to cover my confusion, bar laughter ringing in my ears. On my return I insist we stick to ze business agenda.

Wally explains zat out original sponsor for Eurovision coverage, Craven A TV, was banned unless zer TV logo carried an EC health warning, which zey refused because zey said ze European Commission should pay for ze warning, since it gets 50 per cent of its revenue from tax on cigarettes. So we cannot go on TV, but Radio Addlestone will generously support us if we accept zer own sponsors, who are very ambitious to break into Europe.

'The trouble is,' Wally goes on, 'Radio Addlestone's sponsors are all local and don't have much cash. The candidates are, as usual, our very own privatized Addlestone Sewage Works, which wants to change its image dramatically in order to go into Europe.

In fact, I've just developed a pan-European campaign for zem, but I don't think it goes far enough because zey must strengthen zer image for recycling. I've suggested a new corporate name, "Addlestone Recycled Sewage for Europe" or ARSE for short, with the international slogan, "We Don't Just Take the P out of Europe – We Recycle It!" I think it could work as long as we make it clear each country only consumes its own recyclage, in other words the French consume their own and we consume ours, but there's no cross-frontier fertilization, if you understand me.'

'Brilliant, Wal!' I exclaim, but Sharon is puzzled.

'What's cross-frontier fertilization, you clever boy?'

'Complicated to explain, Sharry,' Wally perseveres. 'Just think it's like you going out with foreigners.'

'Sounds exciting! Like another couple of Spews, gents?' Sharon wraps 'er luminous lime-green fingernails lovingly round ze beer pump and passionately pulls two foaming pints.

'Actually, ladies and gentlemen,' Wally sighs, 'that's the only serious sponsor we have, apart from the radio station itself. Chores might chip in a bit: Cyclops have offered free contact lenses, and the Cloaca Maxima has promised free Spaghetti Svengali, Marmalade Pizza and Rosso Paralitico for you two presenters. That's it. Oh, and Kev's mum-in-law says the Women's Lib Institute will have a whip-round for Addle Stones from their late-night charity work. No big deal.' Ze meeting falls silent, except for ze slurps, for several minutes.

Suddenly, in through ze door walks Jerry Logan, wearing a reflective-pink Savile Row suit and a beaming smile. 'Begorra, what a morning it's been, lads! I'm training this cub announcer, Jimmy Laramie, to stand in for me so I can a take a break or two with you lads from time to time. Mine's a large Spew, Wally, if the advertising world can stretch that far!'

Wally obliges and Jerry, known for 'is gift of ze gob, carries on. 'I tink I've solved our problem, lads, for the Song Contest. But don't congratulate me unless you're prepared to keep slaking me thirst!'

Jerry tells us 'e's got ze support of ze European Karaoke Broadcasting Union to transmit ze Contest to all five participating countries.

'Only five?!' Wally and I exclaim. Jerry explains zat, since we 'ad to abandon ze idea of TV, a lot of countries dropped out, but ze main ones are still in: Lebanon, ze Gaza Strip, Bosnia, ze

Ukraine and Pakistan: Britain will be represented by ze newly privalized Republic of Liverpool, which 'as just been sold off to Ireland.

We are all very happy at Jerry's news and gratefully 'elp 'im back to ze Radio Addlestone studio at ze top of ze CAB Tower just in time to read ze one o'clock news. Wally and I drop down to ze Taxi Tavern where I show 'im my incomprehensible letter from ze GBH bank. 'E is puzzled for a few minutes, zen 'is face lights up.

'I've got it! The reason you can't understand it, Ash, is not because of your English but because it's been written by a computer controlled by Spell-Check. Spell-Check takes what's been written by an executive and corrects all the words it thinks is wrong according to its own interpretation of the general sense – or lack of it, so that the executive doesn't have to check it personally. Let me read it out loud to you, it'll be easier to follow.

"Dear Mr Mango Tout, It is with the deepest sympathy that our Charwoman, Lady Lloyd Berkeley Mid-West has destructed me to put in righting the Bank's revue of your account on which we have run a computer cheque which has been red by our senior-citizen management. They were most upset when they sore your current lack of balance.

"'Although we increase the value" – I think they mean "appreciate",' Wally comments, '"increase the value of your capacity to mainline –" inject?' Wally shrugs, "to mainline freshly laundered funds from your Giro check investments, we must more distantly point out the hole banking system in recent months is going through a difficult menstrual cycle. As you must have red in our financial squeeze the guilt market has gone through its flaw. The wind of change is blowing through international markets and your overdraught situation cannot be allowed to continue so distantly above our Agreed sealing.

"Please understand that you are no longer a loan in this predicatment. The Bank has many commitments to Fourth, and even Fifth, World countries who demand our financial crutch to the melody of many zillions of dollars. As a result we can no longer carry the burden of your £35.42 overdraught and must close your account forthwith.

"If you have difficulty repaying us the conspicuous debt, may we suggest you open a lone account with the National Bank of Outer Mongolia, 26 Main Street, Urumqi, whose debt of

US$10,000,000,000 we have fully underwritten. Yours faithfully. The Great Britain Holdings Bank. – GBH: Nice Business To Do People With: Have a Nice Day –" That's it. Ash, I'm afraid.' Wally 'ands me back ze letter. 'Oh, and that reminds me, Ashy: Kev wants you to meet him at the Commissioner for Oaths office at two-thirty to fix your new name.'

'That's good,' I reply, 'I feel like swearing – officially!'

We say 'au revoir' and less zan an hour later I walk out into ze freezing drizzle a new man: Ashley Peabody. I cannot wait for my very first Giro Cheque. Absinthe will be delighted. Not to mention ze voluptuous Marie Celeste!

Next morning I wake up to find my bucket half full of ice. Ze roof is still leaking of course and I forgot ze hot water-bottle. Out of ze window it is freezing fog, so Rod will not show up again today. I go down stairs to make Absinthe and I a cup of tea; she was out late last night and deserves to be pampered once in a while. Back in bed I read ze morning *Strumpet's* news. Ze front page headline is: 'New Triassic Horror for Schools: *THR*-Saurus!'

Apparently, Runnynose council is to introduce a thesaurus into every classroom to help pupils and zer teachers spell correctly. Another educational reform on page one says zat a new supplementary English GCSE is to be tried out next year, called Social Chat, teaching girl students to handle technical terminology about car exhausts, water cisterns and three-pin plugs, and boy students to understand technical terms associated wiz blow-driers, tampons and which end of babies to put nappies on: ze objective is to 'encourage intellectual intercourse between ze sexes and improve pub conversation'.

Inside ze paper, ze GPO announces it will be improving first-class deliveries (which will shortly increase to 135p) by introducing gears on all postmen's bikes. Ze Non-Working Man's Club is laying astro-turf on its snooker tables to prevent ze baize being always ripped up by ze mis-cueing of its emotional members; astro-turf is also apparently more resistant to lit cigarette ash. Finally, I notice Pees 'n' Queues are advertising pavement sites next to ze level crossing, fully furnished wiz battered old hats and fake pound coins, to ease Runnynose district's housing shortage; cheap mortgages are also being offered on mobile cardboard boxes. How inventive ze British are on zer crowded little island!

On ze way to ze pub through ze driving sleet I notice zat one of Pees' 'n' Queues pavement sites 'as already been taken up by a new resident, so I drop a 20p coin into 'is soggy hat and ask 'im to let me know when 'e's 'aving 'is 'ouse-warming party. I cannot quite understand 'is accent, but 'e seems to invite me to take a flying something at a rolling doughnut. I promise to buy 'im a doughnut on ze way back, and tip my anorak hood as I move hurriedly on to ze Taxi where Kev is waiting for me to sign ze Giro Cheque forms wiz my new signature. 'Ow *magnifique*: a true Brit at last!

Gerry behind ze bar is looking as beautifully jerrybuilt as ever, but nearly in tears. Ze reason is she and Andy 'ave been given notice by ze brewery, Soprano-Coward Breweries, who plan to turn zem out and convert ze Taxi into Britain's first 'Auto Pub'. Andy appears from ze kitchen, also very upset. 'E explains ze new concept to us.

'The Auto Pub will of course make millions for the accountants and maybe the brewers because the Auto Pub will have no staff at all – just machines dispensing booze in cans, from pseudo-real ale to Super lager and gin and tonic for the golfing set. Just put your coins in, press the button and bingo, instant hangovers. 'Course there'll be some semblance of humanity: "barmaid machines" – according to how much you put in you get a video smile or a low lean-forward; after the six o'clock watershed fellows might get even more than that – for a price. They're working on a female version too, for in the Ladies toilet of course. Sad really. But it's the inevitable march of progress of the accountants, ain't it? Can I offer you something while I'm still allowed?'

We all commiserate wiz Andy and Gerry and drink to zer new future as spring water bottle-fillers at Addlestone Recycled Sewage Enterprises. Foolishly, as usual, I ask what about vandalism of ze Auto Pub machines.

'Easy,' Andy replies, 'black-leather-jacketed robots on every door. Not much of an innovation if you think about it.'

Ze afternoons are now very dark and misty damp, so much more restful zan ze warm exhilarating winter nights of Provence! But ze advent of ze exciting English Christmas is getting higher.

In ze High Street, Kev's mum-in-law, Doll, is dressed as Father Christmas in a 'ired red costume – she did not need to 'ire ze white beard, or change 'er voice. She sits on a bar-stool outside ze Oxfam shop and, for 50p each, sweetly invites little children to sit on 'er knee to tell 'er what zey want for Christmas. To ze little girls she tells zem zey will get all things nice; to ze little boys she tells zem zey will get snakes and snails and puppy-dogs' tails in zer Christmas puddings unless zey pay 'er another 50p. At ze end of each day, Kev tells me, she disappears into ze WLI to put 'er spoils into ze 'Bitches' Cauldron, as 'e calls it.

But finally, ze night of ze EuroRadio Karaoke Song Contest arrives. Ze whole of Addlestone is agog and Nadir Tours 'ave generously bused in ze contestants from as far afield as Liverpool and Southal. Accommodation 'as been arranged for all five contestants to share ze luxury suite at ze Coq au Vin which Nigo Bart 'as generously given up for one night. Sharon and I rehearse ze presentation all afternoon in Radio Addlestone's studio, coached by Jerry Logan. At seven prompt, we race through ze freezing sleet to ze Addlestone First Brownie Pack Nissen Hut Hall to take ze stage in front of a huge audience of at least forty excited spectators.

Jerry takes ze microphone to explain zis is ze very first EuroRadio Karaoke Song Contest in mime; ze proceeds will go to a new worldwide relief charity, PUNIFAA, the organization for the Protection of United Nations Forces from Allied Attack, which 'as been in particular need in recent months.

Ze Contest begins and ze *Strumpet* Brownie camera starts flashing. Unfortunately, Sharon is wearing a costume which is far too revealing even for radio, but we manage to introduce all ze contestants without me fluffing my lines.

It is an exhilarating contest wiz amazing results which Sharon and I announce across ze air-waves in reverse order:

'Ukraine: for the song "It's Ukraining in my Heart", sponsored by the Gorbachev Swiss Trust – deux points;

Lebanon: for the song "I'm Bay Rootin' for you, Babe", sponsored by Phoenix Life Assurance – cinq points;

The Gaza Strip: for the song "Oh, Sharon, I am but your Fuel", sponsored by Paul Gascoigne – six points;

Southall-Pakistan: for the song "Love Potion No 9 (from your local chemist)", sponsored by Singh-Along Records – neuf points;

Liverpool: for the song "Giro Can't Buy you Love" – vingt-trois points!'

Liverpool is ze clear winner of ze Addlestone Recycled Sewage Europe Karaoke Mime Award. What an evening and what a triumph for ze former Great Britain! Sharon and I celebrate our success wiz ze contestants in zer suite at ze Coq au Vin. I discreetly draw a veil over ze rest of ze evening because I 'ave no memory of it.

At last it is Christmas Week, and a very busy week it is too. Everything is very festive. Ze Runnynose council 'as bedecked ze High Street wiz fairy lights in ze shape of Giro cheques, ze Oxfam shop is packed wiz 'usbands buying their families and girlfriends presents, and ze pubs are overflowing all day long. 'Ow seriously ze English take zer religious festivals!.

Ze Free Range carol singers visit Five Station Approach singing 'Rudolph the Red-Nosed Reindeer', 'Oh Carol, I am but a Yule' and 'O Come, All Ye Faithful', which I think must be an American cult hymn. Absinthe offers zem traditional hot mince pies, but zey prefer a crate of Spew Extra. We must be a good audience because zey come back every night.

On Christmas Eve, Absinthe and I wrap up and brave ze freezing North wind to go to ze candlelit midnight service at ze Free Range service. Zer is a very special atmosphere tonight because ze animals 'ave been allowed in again, wiz pride of place given to ze sheep and asses in ze front row. We sing 'While Shepherds Wash Their Flocks By Night' and 'Silent Night' to ze traditional accompaniment of Trev ze Rev's guitar wiz Eric Surplice on drums, and zen race back 'ome to get warm wiz a Cornish Patis.

In France we would 'ave our Christmas meal. 'Réveillon', tonight but we plan to save ourselves for ze traditional English Christmas Day lunch. Again, following English folklore, Absinthe and I secretly fill each other a stocking of little presents which we sneak into ze bedroom in ze dark. We go sleep in eager anticipation of what Mother and Father Christmas will bring us.

We are woken next morning by a bright white light shining through ze bedroom curtains. I think we 'ave overslept but when I open ze curtains, *quel miracle*!: everything is covered in snow – my dream come true. A white Christmas! It is very beautiful except zat it hides my railway sidings and Safeways car park. But at least: we can put out some stale crusts for ze lovely birds!

While Absinthe is still sleeping I go downstairs and make a

special traditional French hot punch of Algerian red wine. Fernet Branca and Mandarin orange juice. Upstairs we toast our first English Christmas and open our stockings. Absinthe 'as kindly put mine in ze bucket wiz ze 'ot water-bottle. Alas, among ze other trinkets, like a watch wiz a meal-time alarm and a gold chain wiz my name and address on a large medallion, she 'as bought me a mobile phone, all so zat I can 'keep in contact and people know where to bring me home'.

In Absinthe's stocking she finds a large shatter-proof vanity mirror, a handbag big enough for 'er beloved Eiffel Tower and ze *Feminist Guide To Sex Without Men*. Of course we are both saving ze big present till after lunch.

We 'ave opted for traditional English Christmas fare wiz a nostalgic French touch: instead of roast turkey we are 'aving roast pigeons, which I shot secretly three nights ago as zey were nestling under ze eaves of ze Runnynose town hall. 'Aving been fed on McDonald's throw-aways and other delicious take-away left-overs from all over ze streets of Addlestone, zey are very plump and turn out to be absolutely scrumptious wiz a couple of quail-sized robins marinated in Super Spew on ze side.

Absinthe and I toast each other in our native Provençal cocktail 'Pastis Brut', a sort of Bucks Fizz but made wiz pastis and champagne, and exchange presents. Absinthe gives me a voucher for Macho Mops barbers to start a pony-tail; zey will also pierce my ears (while I wait) and give me a small tattoo on any part of my body. What's more, she also gives me six enormous gold earrings to go wiz ze piercing, three for each ear. I am like ze cow jumping over ze moon!

Zen Absinthe opens 'er present and squeaks wiz joy as she unwraps a latex scale model of ze Leaning Tower of Pisa. I knew she would appreciate ze artistry of another classical monument.

'I nearly got you ze Empire State Building, pet,' I tell 'er, but she shakes her head.

'No, *cheri*, zis is much more monumental,' she purrs, 'in any case, I don't like too many sharp edges on buildings. And ze angle of ze tower is so cute!' I 'ave obviously earned my Christmas kiss.

We spend ze rest of ze day sleepily digesting. Wiz some 'elp from Addlestone's very own Armanlegnac. I doze through most of Her Maj's Christmas message, but I understand 'er 'annus' is still a problem. Zer is no point in going out for a drink tonight, because zis is ze one sacred day of ze year when, traditionally, Englishmen stay in wiz zer families, so about nine o'clock we succumb to ze heart-warming spirit of ze English Christmas and clamber up ze stairs to prepare for ze morrow's festive hangover. I wake up wiz an enormous thudding in my brain. As I stagger down ze stairs to grab one of Al Dente's very effective Italian antihangover suppositories – 'Dim-Innuendo' – I gradually realize ze banging is not in my head but is coming from ze roof. I look through ze window to see Rod's van wiz piles of roof tiles in ze front yard. What a day to arrive! But zey must not be sent away! I dress quickly and step out into ze snowy back garden. Rod is on ze roof and ze Cleavage lads are getting ze tiles up to 'im. We exchange shouted greetings and I ask Rod 'ow it is ze snow is more clement for roof tiling zan all ze other elements we 'ave 'ad recently.

'Sorry, Monsieur Ash,' Rod shouts back. 'Just 'ad to risk it. The wife's parents are staying with us, and their kids. It's bedlam. I'd rather commit suicide than stay indoors with that lot, whatever the weather. Won't take long, though. Should be finished by lunchtime. Wouldn't half help, Monsieur Ash, if you could spare some of your famous hot Brute Pastis punch. It's quite parky up here.'

I waste no time obliging, and Rod comes down ze ladder to drink a foaming goblet. 'Honest, Ash, I promise I didn't peek when your wife got out of bed. But you must've given her a good seeing to last night,' Rod gives me 'is winking grin. I tell 'im I do not understand. 'Well she seemed very unsteady on her pins!' This time 'e gives me ze full nudge and 'is lads try to stifle their guffows.

Ze punch works: ze whole job is finished by opening time. I should 'ave served it in April straight after ze storm. Of course we must all celebrate zis breakthrough in British efficiency, but down ze Taxi Tavern, because Rod 'as been banned from ze Dog and Duck for giving Sharon excessive compliments within Bruiser Reade's earshot.

I am so relieved to 'ave ze roof done I offer everybody a drink. Not such a dangerous move as it turns out, because everyone is at home licking zer wounds and saving zer Giro money for New Year's Eve, so ze bar is practically empty. At least until Rodge ze Dodge bursts in full of seasonal joy. Rod bends my ear: 'His hangover won't hit him till half way through January'.

'What's concurring, then, to occasion this celebration so soon

135

after Christmas?' Rodge can smell ze free alcohol.

'I'm celebrating 'aving a roof over my 'ead – after nine months of tribulation. Please join us,' I offer, realizing he is already in a Super Spew mood, and we all toast Rod and 'is super-efficient team.

'The one thing about being a born-again bachelor,' Rodge starts off, being a dyed-in-ze-wool divorcee, 'you can't get nagged, unless of course you're daft enough to get trapped again.'

'You're just a misogynist, Rodge,' I venture.

'Misogynist?' 'E explodes a mouthful of Spew across ze bar, narrowly missing Gerry's cleavage. 'Don't you insult me, Ash! I'm not that much of a wimp! I'm as much in favour of sexual equality and role reversal as the next man. Why, I don't mind being pampered every day after I done the hoovering and wiped the baby's bottom a couple of times. Can't wait to be lying back on the settee in a loose kaftan eager to welcome the big woman home with a cheeseburger languishing in the microwave. Paradise! 'Course I wouldn't mind staying in the macho role if I was guaranteed a pension at sixty and death at eighty-five with ten years' more life expectancy and fifteen years' more pension than I can look forward to now. Touch me up another Spew, Ash, will you, while I go for a gypsy?'

And off 'e storms as Kev shuffles in wearing dark glasses and an expression to match. 'What's all this?' 'e grunts: 'Rodge pontificating out of his "ex cathedra" again?'

As Rodge returns to Kev's disparaging gaze, I step forward to try to calm ze waters, feeling as useful as a UN commander in a battle zone. 'Come on, gentlemen, zis is ze season of good will. We must put aside all hostile feelings. I and my wife 'ave been welcomed 'ere by all of you – even by Rodge's xenophobia'.

'I've never been to Japan!' chips in Rodge, quick as a flash, and gives me ze best nudge for ages, dead-shot into ze Gents. I am surprised to see new condom machines 'ere, selling a range I 'ave never seen before, called 'Access': ze regular model is ze 'Black & Decker Pile-Driver', but zer is also a festive design wiz a luminous inscription round it – 'Happy Aniversary' – what a silly misprint! I quickly buy a packet of each as an extra Christmas treat for Absinthe and return to ze guffaws in ze bar.

I am surprised to find ze gathering now besotted by an orgy of bonhomie. Everyone buys Absinthe and I a drink and Rod, who is a keen allotment gardener between fair-weather building assignments, offers to give us some of 'is 'orgasmically' grown carrots, which brings an eager light into Absinthe's eyes, so of course we accept willingly.

We part our separate ways in ze early dusk but not before Absinthe and I 'ave been invited by Kev to ze Dog and Duck's New Year's Eve party. It is fun trudging back 'ome through ze refreshing snow under ze twinkling stars zat shine down on Addlestone.

New Year's Eve arrives, and Absinthe and I put on our best casual dress for ze Dog and Duck party – Spew-proof jeans suits which can be binned tomorrow if ze stains cannot be removed – and struggle through ze lovely brown slush to ze pub. After last year's novice experience we 'ave eaten one of our starling and sparrow pies from ze freezer, washed down wiz ze remaining bottle of Al Donte's pink Nasti Spumanta so zat we need not worry about food or drink later on.

When we get inside ze Dog and Duck no familiar faces are in sight, and I say to Absinthe zey must be getting their tank up somewhere else first. But suddenly, from ze Function Room at ze back, Kev appears resplendent in festive dress, ie, 'is usual perforated jeans and low-cut open shirt, but wiz a comic hat.

'E welcomes us wiz open arms, 'We thought you'd never get here, Ash, Abs! Come with me!' And we are ushered into ze Function Room where, to our astonishment, all our friends are sitting round four long tables in a square. Zey cheer and jeer as we enter, and everybody is wearing funny hats and clinging on to zer Gutterspew pints for sheer life, men and women alike.

Kev takes us to ze middle seats on ze top table, where two fancy hats and two pints of Gutterspew await us. Everyone is zer: Mave ze Rave (as Absinthe tells me she is now known at ze WLI) and Doll, at ze opposite end of ze room to Kev who is next to Absinthe; Rod and Cleave; Wally and Shirl; Sharon and Bruiser; ze Brain, Al Stein, Winston Thatcher. Andy Lyons, Bernie Pire, Rick ze Dick, Twiggie and no less a dignitary zan Mayor Cliff Oakes himself; but ze real surprise is Rodge, sitting two places from me at ze top table next to sweet little Cher Flashit. But ze place between me and Rodge is empty – until, through ze door walks a vision of voluptuousness in a diaphanous black frilled frock and underwear to match wiz a white rose, for purity I can only assume, in her beautifully blonded hair – Marie Celeste. She sidles over and wriggles into ze seat beside me. What a joyous occasion zis promises to be!

Gutterspew follows Gutterspew, and Phnom Pen Nib brings in fresh cartons of 'is famous 'Specific Prawn Curry' take-away. Suddenly Kev struggles to 'is feet and raps on ze newspaper tablecloth wiz 'is spoon, calling for silence:

'Ladies, gents and girlfriends, the purpose of this knees-up tonight is of course to welcome the New Year in. But it is also a speical occasion. Exactly one year ago to this day Addlestone was invaded by aliens. These aliens were none other than Achille and Absinthe Mange-Tout, who had fled the chaos and squalor of Provence to settle on the sleepy, eyedyllic shores of the river Addle.' Applause all round. 'At first we were suspicious of these aliens but gradually, as we got to know them, we became terrified of them!' Chuckles all round. 'We soon realized the Mange-Touts were a force to be reckoned with. Ash became a founding member of the Addlestone Open University and taught us all to be bilingual.'

'What's that,' Rodge butts in, 'satisfying two women at the same time?' Guffaws.

'No, that's schizophallic!' Al Stein corrects.

'You're dyxlexic, Al, that's your trouble!' ze Brain splutters through 'is rolled fag. More guffaws.

'Thank you, Brain,' Kev continues. 'Absinthe became a leading light in the WLI and raised lots of Addle Stones for charity. And, of course, the Mange-Touts helped in the political coup of the year: my election as councillor and potential mayor.'

Boos all round and a frown above Cliff Roakes' cigar. 'Above all, the Mange-Touts taught us French fair play – or "faites vos jeux" as you call it. The barbarity of the St Hillians' Hunt was exposed humanely and efficiently. And we have been introduced to French delicacies like croissant slug-burgers and frogspawn toasties.

'You have well earned the Freedom of Addlestone, Ash. But now the final accolade! On behalf of the Runnynose Council I proudly present you with ... your very first Giro Cheque!' Applause all round.

I am flabbygasted and overjoyed, especially when Marie Celeste leans over and gives me a big sloppy kiss. I stand up wiz quivering knees to deliver an inadequate reply, but ze room

138

begins to spin and everything goes hazy. Next thing I remember, I wake up sitting in ze bar wiz Marie Celeste pouring Gutterspew onto a bar cloth to mop my brow. Marie tells me it was ze emotion of ze occasion, but I revive rapidly after two glasses of Armanlegnac.

The evening proceeds apace. I dance wiz Marie Celeste while Rodge sleeps wiz Cherry on ze dance floor, snoring wiz 'is 'ead flopped on 'er shoulder; ze Brain dances wiz Doll, keeping 'is pint in 'is 'and and kissing 'er cheek wiz 'is fag still in 'is mouth; Absinthe dances wiz Mave and seems to really enjoy 'erself; Kev and Cliff prop up ze bar and keep ze drinks flowing. At ten to midnight, ze TV is switched on and we switch to Babycham Extra-Strong. On ze stroke of midnight ze toasts and ze kisses fly and we 'old each other up in ze Auld Lang Syne shuffle. Some time later, becase all ze Zimmerframes 'ave been booked, Absinthe and I 'elp each other stagger through ze cooling drizzle back to Five Station Approach. One obligatory pastis nightcap and we retire gratefully wiz my Giro Cheque under my pillow.

New Year's Day dawns late at Five Station Approach. As well it might: it is sleeting snow cats and huskies outside. Ze *Addlestone Strumpet's* 'eadline is 'Lordy me, Ma'am!' In ze New Year's Honours List, Her Maj 'as given every Member of Parliament a peerage to clear out ze House of Commons completely and start again! She is cleverer zan I 'zought.

The New Year promises to be as exciting as last. Encore Bonne Anneé. Addlestone!